CW00382490

Rather a Mixed Crowd*

Military Medicine in India and
South East Asia
1944-1947

John Black, M.D., F.R.C.P.

* A derogatory term for the Royal Army Medical Corps used by
Regular Army Officers

William Sessions Limited
York, England

ISBN 1 85072 309 5

Printed in 11 on 12 point Plantin
from Author's Disk
by Sessions of York
The Ebor Press
York, England

Contents

Chapter   *Page*

    List of Illustrations   iv

    Preface   iv

    Acknowledgements   v

I   Luck with the Membership (M.R.C.P.) examination –
the Royal Army Medical Corps (R.A.M.C.) –
Tropical medicine in Edinburgh – By ship to India   1

II   Introduction to India – Bangalore – Slow train across
India to Assam – Wingate's Chindits   7

III   A chance meeting in Calcutta – Teaching Army
medicine in Poona – Visit to battle zone – Dacca   16

IV   News of the atom bomb – Singapore and the
prisoners of war   26

V   Malaya after the war – Burma again –
Return to a cold U.K.   37

    Appendix – The origins and history of the Indian
Medical Service and the Indian Army Medical Corps   50

    Index   57

List of Illustrations

		Page
Map 1 –	India and Bangladesh 1944-1945	vi
Map 2 –	Burma 1945 and 1946-1947	vii
Map 3 –	Malaysia and Singapore 1945-1946	viii
Plate 1 –	Recently arrived in Bangalore, India, with new uniforms	8
Plate 2 –	The author building an oven for the Officers' Mess, Golaghat, Assam, India, April 1944	11
Plate 3 –	Visiting card of a Chinese Colonel	17
Plate 4 –	Crossing the Sittang River, Burma, with 64 Field Company. Madras Sappers and Miners, May 5th, 1945	23
Plate 5 –	The surrender of the Japanese Army, Singapore, September 12th, 1945	27
Fig. 1 –	Part of the case sheet of a sergeant in the Royal Dutch Army while a patient in Changi Gaol Hospital	33
Plate 6 –	A patient with a locally recruited nurse, 24 I.G.H. (C), Malacca, Malaysia, December 1945	38
Plate 7 –	Japanese prisoner of war camp. Johor Bahru, Malaysia, 1946	42
Fig. 2 –	Graph of the incidence of malaria in the Japanese Prisoner of War Camp at Prome, Burma, 1946-1947	45
Fig. 3 –	Figure reproduced from the "Official History of the Indian Armed Forces in the Second World War 1935-45"	55

Preface

BECAUSE LITTLE has been written about the army medical services in India and South East Asia during and after the second World War, I thought it would be of interest to record the experience of a junior officer in the Royal Army Medical Corps during three years in India, Burma and what is now called Malaysia.

iv

Acknowledgements

I AM INDEBTED to Mr Stephen Rose of P & O for information on the history and tonnage of the S.S. Stratheden and to Miss J M Wraight of the Maritime Information Centre at the National maritime Museum, Greenwich, London, for allowing me access to the "Nautical Reports" which contained the records of the Stratheden's voyage from Liverpool to Bombay in February 1944. I wish to thank the Friends of the Wellcome Library and Centre for the History of Medicine for a generous grant towards the production of this book and the Army Medical Directorate for permission to reproduce the R.A.M.C. badge. I am particularly grateful to Sandra Parfitt for her care and skill in typing the numerous versions of this book.

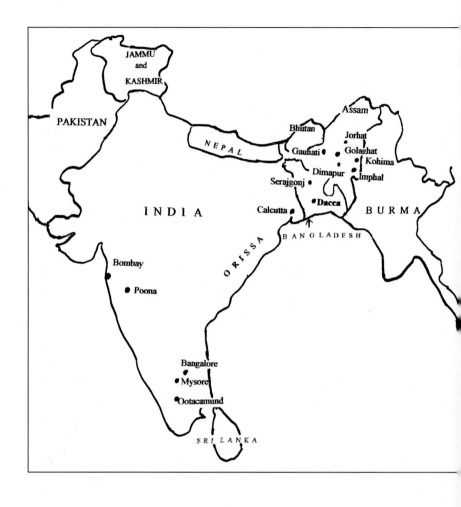

Map 1 – INDIA AND BANGLADESH
1944-1945 (modern boundaries).

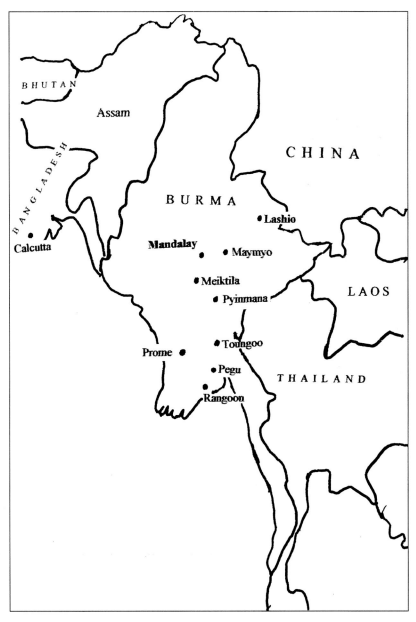

Map 2 – BURMA
1945 and 1946-1947 (modern boundaries).

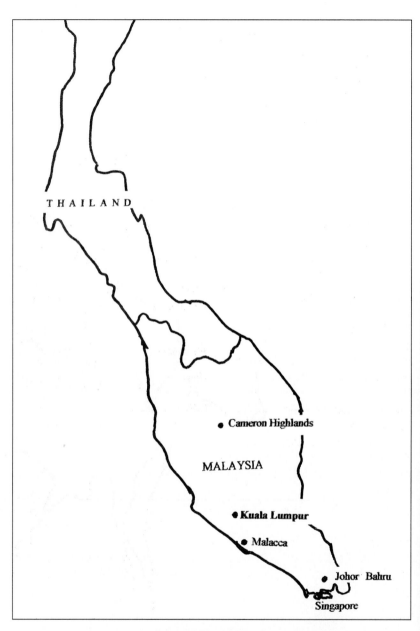

Map 3– MALAYSIA AND SINGAPORE
1945-1946

viii

I

Luck with the Membership (M.R.C.P.) examination – The Royal Army Medical Corps (R.A.M.C.) – Tropical medicine in Edinburgh – By ship to India

AFTER QUALIFYING at University College Hospital in June 1942 I held two junior posts, the second at the E.M.S. (Emergency Medical Service) Base Hospital in Hemel Hempstead where I worked as House Surgeon to Mr Twistington Higgins, the Paediatric Surgeon, and as House Physician to Dr Geoffrey Gillam, a cardiologist, and to Dr Hugh Dunlop, a mildly eccentric man, interested in neurology. Over coffee one morning Dr Dunlop asked me my views on the function of the fastigiobulbar tract; I don't know what I said, but he seemed satisfied. Both he and Geoffrey Gillam encouraged me to "Have a go" at the Membership* examination (M.R.C.P.); as they put it, "When you come out of the Army, your brains will be completely addled, so why not try now?" At that time one could sit Membership as soon after qualifying as one liked, so I took their advice and worked hard at the books.

There was one snag however, I might be called up before I had time to sit the papers and practicals in October 1943. I received my "call up" papers and attended for my "medical" at Millbank in September. Vaguely hoping it might do some good, I put on my old school tie. The white-coated colonel who was examining me suddenly put down his stethoscope and said, "Which house were you in?"

---

* The examination to become a Member of the Royal College of Physicians of London was then, as now, essential for anyone wishing to become a Consultant in one of the medical specialities.

1

"Trevelyan" I replied, "My dear chap, so was I. Is there anything I can do for you?" he said. So I asked him if my "call-up" could be delayed until November to give me time to take the M.R.C.P. examination. He apparently fixed it and to my great surprise I passed. Having nothing to lose, I made a number of daring guesses in the pathology examination and was lucky in the clinical part of the examination in which I was given as a "short case" a man with thrombosis of the posterior inferior cerebellar artery whom I had seen staggering ataxically about at the far end of the room, as someone's "long case", so it was easy to make the correct diagnosis.

Apart from these strokes of luck, I made a tactical mistake in completing my questionnaire to the R.A.M.C. by putting down "fluent French and German" (quite wrong), hoping that this could ensure that I would not be send to India. It was only later that I learned to manipulate the Army's "perversity principle". I should have expressed a preference for the 14th Army.

Medical officers were automatically given a commission as a lieutenant, but had to undergo an initial training course at the R.A.M.C. depot at Crookham, in Hampshire. This involved elementary drill and lectures on army organisation and military medicine, and an assault course watered down for medical officers. One of the lectures, on medicine in a cold climate, was by a young captain, bent like a wind-blown tree. We later discovered that he had spent some time in Greenland where the continuous winter gales, we thought, had caused his posture. We did a number of small group exercises; in one of these we were taken in a bus with its windows blacked out, dumped in the middle of the Hampshire countryside and told to find our way back to Crookham as quickly as possible. We were forbidden to ask any questions, and all signposts had been removed, to confuse invading Germans. I had an idea; the tombstones in the villages would tell us where we were. After this we had no difficulty in finding our way and were the first group back. At the end of the course we were each interviewed by the manic Chief Instructor, who told me, "Unless you muck in more, you'll never make a good Unit Medical Officer". I never did become a Unit Medical Officer.

After Crookham I was sent, with about thirty other new medical officers, on a course of tropical medicine in Edinburgh.

2

Edinburgh, presumably because we all came from the South. "Bunny" Helm and I rather fancied ourselves at squash and accepted a challenge from the secretary of the University Squash Club, an Edinburgh girl who took us on, one after the other, and beat us easily.

It was now early December and we all wanted to do our Christmas shopping on what was almost certainly our last Christmas before going overseas. I suggested that we should make out a rota, with a constant number of people absent at each lecture, with those attending signing for the absentees. This ensured that the class was always the same size and the lecturers would notice nothing wrong; it worked splendidly.

We learned a lot about the mouthparts and sexual organs of mosquitoes, but little about mepacrine (for the prevention of malaria), nor indeed much of practical tropical medicine. Of the lecturers the most interesting personality was Professor Percy Lelean. A small man with a shiny brown bald head, he had served in the Army in India and Egypt during the 1914-18 war and had written a well-known textbook on military sanitation.[1] He described to us a number of sanitary appliances such as the "Serbian Barrel", a disinfector which had been used in Gallipoli and was still included in the Indian Army's 1945 edition of "Field Service Hygiene Notes".[2] He had invented a "portable inclined plane incinerator"[1] and "Lelean's Sack"[3] for disinfecting water bottles, which was used in Egypt in 1919. None of these seemed to have much relevance to the Army in 1943.

In retrospect, the course was pretty useless. Word must have got round about this because the A.D.M.S. (Assistant Director of Medical Services) of the Edinburgh District summoned me to his office to ask my opinion of the course (there were excellent courses in London and Liverpool). Having nothing to compare it with, and in awe of the red tab of a full colonel I told him that the course was satisfactory. Luckily he didn't believe me, and the course was stopped shortly after.

After Edinburgh I was posted to a C.R.S. (Camp Reception Station) at Westcliff-on-Sea on the Essex coast. I was fortunate in my Commanding Officer, Major Brian Pollock, an eccentric but efficient regular officer who regarded the Army as an enjoyable madhouse, an attitude which helped me greatly over the following years. Brian Pollock's lecture to the "other ranks" on sex and venereal disease was a masterpiece of commonsense and bawdy humour. "Beware of the little blue-eyed angels, they're the ones who will give you the clap". His advice on avoiding an accusation of rape was "lips first, then breasts, and then you can start".

My first two weeks at the C.R.S. were quiet, and I was able to attend, on one afternoon a week, the medical out-patients at Southend General Hospital where I saw my first and only case of Adie's Syndrome, unusually, in a male. Suddenly we were inundated with units straight from Italy. They had all three sorts of lice and most of them had malaria. One of their sergeants kindly explained to me that body lice lay their eggs in the seams of clothing, something I hadn't been told about at Crookham or Edinburgh.

In February 1944 came embarkation leave. After this I was sent to the R.A.M.C. depot at Beckett's Park in Leeds where I "drew" my tropical kit which consisted of a camp bed, folding chair, canvas bath, canvas bucket, bed roll, a pair of baggy shorts, long khaki socks, a shapeless bush jacket and a topee in a cloth bag. We were also issued with a revolver, because Japan had not signed the Geneva Convention on the non-combatant role of medical personnel. In the early morning we rocked our way to the station in a convoy of trams for the train to Liverpool.

We embarked on the S.S. Stratheden, a P. & O. ship of 23,772 tons, built at Barrow in 1936. We had all seen pictures of the 14th Army in Burma (Myanmar)* with their bush hats, and knew that topees were "out". Where it started I do not know, but within a few minutes of embarkation hundreds of topees were bobbing about in the Mersey. The Stratheden was designed to carry 530 first class and 450 tourist class passengers. We left Liverpool, in convoy, at 4pm on February 21st 1944 with 4330 troops and a few civilians on board. For officers the accommodation was cramped but not unpleasant, with four in a small cabin. For the "other ranks", the conditions were appalling; in the mess decks the men slept in hammocks which were almost touching. It was surprising that there

---

* In deference to recent changes in place names or spelling I have inserted the new names on the first occasion when they occur in the text, but have otherwise retained the original form.

4

were no epidemics of any sort. The only problems were sea sickness in the Mediterranean and prickly heat in the Red Sea.

Among my draft of R.A.M.C. Officers was Lieutenant Hermann Lehman.* A cultured and widely read man, he introduced me to Kafka by way of "The Castle".

There was little in the way of entertainment; an ENSA party including Emlyn Williams, the author, was on board but they never offered to entertain us; probably they were glad of a rest. We were bored, and a few of decided to put out a rumour that we were going to India (which was pretty obvious anyway) to see how long it would take to return to its originators. It took exactly thirty six hours, during which the ship's officers put out an angry message on the Tannoy about the dangers of rumour-mongering. Apart from this foolishness, we had the task of censoring letters, cutting out any parts which might contain information likely to be useful to the enemy. In our naivety we cut out acronyms such as BOLTOP and SWALK, which we later discovered meant "Better on lips than on paper" and "Sealed with a loving kiss". Probably the recipients thought their loved ones were party to important strategic information.

As another example of the "perversity principle" we were taught Urdu (at a stage when it was conceded that we could only be going to India) by a former lecturer in German who had spent a short time in India. We learned to count up to ten and how to shoo away troublesome Indian children. Among the valuable pieces of information he gave us were "Always keep the grass round your bungalow short because of snakes", and "Shake out your shoes in the morning before you put them on; they may contain a scorpion". He hoped that we had all brought our tennis rackets; I hadn't brought mine, but bought one later in Poona (Pune).

In the early hours of March 6th we saw the low-lying outline of Port Said and smelled the smell of the east, a mixture of coffee, cigarettes and spices. At Port Said some of the troops disembarked and were replaced by glamorous Wrens (W.R.N.S.) destined for Mountbatten's Headquarters in Kandy, in what is now Sri Lanka. We were not allowed to go ashore but the civilians did so and

---

* Later to become a world expert on haemoglobinopathies and Professor of Clinical Biochemistry at Cambridge.

5

returned with exotic purchases from Simon Artz' famous shop. We were however entertained by the traditional visit of a "Gulli-Gulli" man, an Egyptian conjurer.

Two days later we left Port Said and arrived at Suez where we took on board a contingent of American soldiers with the largest packs and kitbags I have ever seen. Leaving Suez on March 10th with 4557 men and women on board we passed through the Suez Canal and the Red Sea and arrived at Aden where we refuelled. At that time Aden was a major port for "coaling" ships. The bunkers were filled by long lines of coolies, climbing up from a lighter to the ship's side by a ladder, each man carrying a load of coal in a basket on his head. We left Aden on March 13th and berthed at Alexandra Dock, in Bombay (Mumbai) on March 20th. We queued for hours for our documents and posting orders which were distributed by a captain in the Royal Scots who greeted us with "Welcome to this unhappy country". His pale blue eyes had the blank look of someone who has died inwardly.

REFERENCES
1. Lelean P S. Sanitation in War. 2nd ed. J A Churchill: London 1957.
2. Medical Directorate, General Headquarters, India. Field Service Hygiene Notes, India. New Delhi; 1945; 438-40.
3. Hammond Searle A C. Sterilization of water bottles by means of the Lelean sack. Journal of the Royal Army Medical Corps 1928; 51; 287-92.

II

Introduction to India – Bangalore – Slow train through
India to Assam – Wingate's Chindits

THE DOCKSIDE and railway station at Bombay were a cultural
shock, with dozens of porters, wearing only a scarlet smock, com-
peting to carry our tin trunks and bedding rolls which they hoisted
onto their heads. Hermann Lehman and I were posted to the
B.M.H. (British Military Hospital) Bangalore, 900 km to the south
of Bombay; this was on the 5ft 6in broad gauge railway and the first
line in the world to use welded track, because of the constancy of
the temperature all the year round. As we passed through Poona
Hermann knelt up on his seat, saying excitedly, "Look, John,
Poona".

On arrival at the B.M.H. we were met by the Adjutant of the
hospital who looked at our ill-fitting shorts and bush jackets and
said, "The first thing you need is a dursi (tailor)". I never again
wore the shorts but eventually wore the bush jacket tucked into my
trousers when I felt I had reached sufficient seniority to wear more
or less what I liked.

Bangalore was a classic military cantonment town, maintained
under British jurisdiction in the, at that time, native state of Mysore
(now in Karnataka) since 1881. The military quarters were in traditional style, with spacious barracks, bungalows, and officers'
messes fronted by imposing white pillars. In our quarters we were
looked after by Indian bearers wearing spotless white uniforms with
a sash in the R.A.M.C. colours and a pagri (turban) with a
R.A.M.C. flash. Each morning we were woken by a bearer with
chota hasri (little breakfast) consisting of tea and a banana. For
breakfast we had two fried eggs; illogically, after years of rationing,
I felt affronted at this extravagance. Shortly after my arrival I heard

7

Plate 1
Recently arrived in Bangalore, India, with new uniforms. The author is in the centre. March 1944.

drums beating and wondered whether the "natives" were in revolt; however they were probably celebrating the feast of Holi.

I was allocated to the Officers' Ward in the B.M.H. and it soon became obvious that the R.A.M.C. officers in Bangalore were only too well adapted to what was essentially a peace time existence. Among the sights of the town was an Italian "maior speziale" (medical specialist) dressed in an immaculate white uniform and gold braid who could be seen sipping a mid-morning cup of coffee in one of the cafés. Though technically prisoners of war, the possibility of escape was so remote that the Italians were allowed a considerable amount of freedom, and many of them acted as orderlies in the hospitals.

I had only been in Bangalore for a week when I was seized with a high fever, acute abdominal pain, and profuse diarrhoea and was admitted to hospital with bacillary dysentery. A few days after my admission, we were inspected by General Claude Auchinleck, Commander in Chief, India. The hospital R.S.M. (regimental sergeant major) instructed the patients on correct procedure: beds were to be made up and we were to lie on top of the sheets until just before the general entered the ward when we were to shuffle under the bedclothes, without disturbing them. On the command, "Lie at attention" we had to lie stiffly in bed until the great man had passed.

My treatment consisted of the traditional mixture of sodium and magnesium sulphate by mouth, supposedly to wash the toxins out of the intestinal tract. This it presumably did, but inevitably the diarrhoea persisted and there seemed no way out of this iatrogenic vicious circle. After five days of this treatment I was feeling well and decided to take the Italian orderly into my confidence and asked him to continue to record my treatment on the chart but not to give me the purgatives. Within forty eight hours the diarrhoea stopped, and I was discharged, thin but "formed". This type of treatment must have caused a considerable drain on manpower.

On my return to duty I was visited on the ward by Lieutenant Colonel J N (Jerry) Morris,* the Officer in Charge of the Medical Division (O.C. Medical Division) of the 600 bedded 38 B.G.H. (British General Hospital) which was about to leave for Assam. I had by now realised that India was capable of swallowing up an unlimited amount of manpower and I had not come thousands of miles to have chota hasris and tiffins (light lunch) brought to me by bearers, so I agreed enthusiastically to join 38 B.G.H.

We entrained in good order at Bangalore Station, taking our quartermaster, Captain Bartlett ("Bart"), in the acute stage of bacillary dysentery, with us on a stretcher. Junior officers travelled in large open coaches with "let down" bunks. I was astonished to find that none of my companions had ever opened a tin in their lives. This was important because in the early stages of the journey we lived on bully beef and ration biscuits; hot water for tea came from the engine. Later, Jerry Morris, as mess president, telegraphed ahead to suitable stations to order fried eggs which he reckoned were safe from bacterial contamination. The train sauntered across India, with innumerable stops in sidings to allow the scheduled trains to pass. One morning we woke to find that the coach containing the sergeants' mess had been shunted away; whether this

---

* Later Professor of Public Health, London School of Hygiene and Tropical Medicine.

was due to incompetence or sabotage we never found out. As we chugged slowly through Orissa the embankments were lined with gaunt adults and pot-bellied children (it was only a few months after the famine of 1943); we threw them packets of ration biscuits, but no-one picked them up. Perhaps they thought the biscuits contained beef products, or they ate them when we had passed. Reaching the outskirts of Calcutta (Kolkata) at night we passed blast furnaces, lighting up the sky.

Finally, we arrived at Howrah (Haora) Station, Calcutta. The whole journey had taken a week. It was necessary to transfer at Calcutta from the broad gauge to the metre gauge Bengal and Assam (B & A) Railway at Sealdah Station. The B. & A. was in poor shape; designed to serve the tea plantations of Assam, it was now carrying troops and supplies to the front in the north of Assam, and was functioning beyond its capacity. We were astonished to see American engineers on the footplates of the locomotives, shovelling coal in the intense heat and humidity. From time to time we passed whole trains which had broken down, or become derailed, and had been pulled off the track and were lying on their sides beside the line.

After three days of sluggish progress we arrived at Serajgonj on the Bramahputra where we were to board a steamer for Gauhati (Guwahati). We watched while hundreds of stretcher cases were unloaded from the decks; they looked like the casualties of a defeated army. We were not allowed on board until the decks had been hosed clean of faeces and vomit. At this point the Bramahputra is about a mile wide and is constantly changing its course; at night navigation was by a searchlight in the bows which picked out the guide poles on the bank or stuck in the riverbed. At Gauhati we disembarked and got on another train for the railhead at Dimapur. At Lumding we stopped for food and tea, and found the station full of tall Chinese soldiers, with their packs supported by head-bands.

The plan was to set up the hospital on the polo ground at Jorhat, about 70 km north of Dimapur. Though the thunder of the guns from the crucial battle for Kohima 140 km to the south could be clearly heard, the local tea planters refused to allow us to use their polo ground for the hospital or their club house for the officers' mess. Jorhat was close to the American air base for planes to China, and we could see the Dakotas and B29's climbing to achieve the necessary height to go over the "hump" (Himalayas) to China.

After this setback, a new site was found at Golaghat about 50 km south of Jorhat. It was now April and the heat and humidity were almost intolerable. Prickly heat made life very uncomfortable and we were allowed to work without shirts. Tanning of the skin alleviated the prickly heat, but those with red hair continued to suffer severely. The humidity was so great that everything, clothing, boots, and books, grew mould, often overnight. Termites attacked from below the piles of British Medical Journals which had wandered across India, but they never ate the Lancet, a tribute to its high quality paper perhaps. While we were sweltering in the heat we could see the snow-covered foothills of the Himalayas about 200 km to the north.

As its name implies, 38 B.G.H. served only British troops. We were lucky in having distinguished senior officers. Our

Plate 2
The author building an oven for the Officers' Mess, Golaghat, Assam, India, April 1944.

11

Commanding Officer was a gentle Orcadian, Colonel R. A. ('Tony') Bennett, who had the engaging habit of dropping his G's. Later he became Director of Medicine and Consultant Physician to the Army with the rank of Major General; after he retired from the Army he was appointed Deputy Surgeon to the Royal Hospital, Chelsea. Jerry Morris, the O.C. Medical Division, an epidemiologist, was an excellent clinician and a dynamic personality; as mess president he ensured that we did not develop scurvy by arranging the local purchase of fresh vegetables and lychees. He also insisted that we took salt tablets with our drinking water, to avoid heat exhaustion from salt depletion. Philip Hawe, the O.C. Surgical Division, was an excellent general surgeon from Liverpool.*

We were of course taking mepacrine daily, as a malaria suppressant. Fortunately the local mosquitoes, though vicious did not carry malaria; they were scarcely deterred by anti-mosquito cream, which was in any case unpleasant to use. I was bitten so many times that ever since mosquito bites fail to produce a lump.

Entertainment was scarce; we had a visit from Elsie and Doris Waters ("Gert and Daisy") which was greatly appreciated. General Slim's wife, a very elegant creature in the khaki uniform of the W.A.C.I.s (Women's Auxillary Corps, India) also visited the hospital.

For a few weeks after we had set up the hospital, things were quiet, and I was "lent" for a week to a neighbouring M.F.T.U. (Malaria Forward Treatment Unit) where the initial treatment for all cases of falciparum (malignant tertian) malaria was an intravenous injection of quinine. At this time we were receiving casualties from local units and from the Kohima-Imphal front. In these British troops malaria was rare, as it had become a military offence not to take the daily mepacrine. We had a few cases of scrub (mite borne) typhus, bacillary and amoebic dysentery, and hepatitis A. Psychiatric casualties were few; one was a R.S.M. with amnesia for recent events; another was a private with loss of sensation in his trigger finger. At Jerry Morris' suggestion I gave them pentothal, to discover the underlying problem. The R.S.M. had been unable to forgive himself for directing fire on to some of his own men, and the private turned out to be illiterate and was in an anxiety state because he was unable to read messages and orders.

---

* Later Consultant Surgeon to the David Lewis Northern Hospital in Liverpool.

The unit had its own casualties; the appalling climate put a strain on everyone, especially the older members. The hospital registrar, a Major Price, in his mid-fifties, suffered terribly from prickly heat and insomnia, and had to be evacuated to India. More worrying was the breakdown of our pathologist. We woke up one morning to find his tent surrounded by a fence of sticks and wire which he had ordered his batman to put up "To keep the Indians out". It was clear that he was suffering from a paranoid delusional state. He was also evacuated and ultimately made a complete recovery. In his absence I was ordered to do an autopsy on one of my own patients who had died from scrub typhus. My objections were overruled. Probably because I was upset at having to cut up my patient, I pricked my finger on a spicule of bone. Feeling ashamed to admit this lapse to Jerry Morris, I timidly approached Colonel Bennett and asked his advice. Whether he really knew the answer, I do not know, but he reassured me. Nothing happened, but I spent an anxious two weeks.

In June there were the first indications of the monsoon. Huge black clouds gathered, followed by violent thunderstorms with hailstones as big as ping-pong balls. Then sheets of rain began to fall and the temperature dropped suddenly. The rain had the startling effect that everyone took off their clothes and stood naked outside their tents in the cooling downpour. However, when the monsoon was fully established the humidity increased and the dirt roads round the hospital became seas of mud. The Tilley lamps in the officers' mess attracted hundreds of moths and evil-smelling beetles which fell into our beer and soup.

During this period the only information we received about the progress of the war was obtained officially from the Army newspaper "SEAC" (South East Asia Command) and from the radio station "All India Radio", whose call signature tune curiously, was a couple of bars from Mendelsohn's Fingal's Cave (Hebrides Overture). Unofficially, we relied on rumour and accounts from neighbouring units and patients evacuated from the front.

On July 21st 1944 we received the first of four convoys from the second Wingate (Chindit) Expedition who had been operating for five months behind the Japanese lines. In all, 401 officers and men were admitted. Jerry Morris, in a paper published in the Journal of the Royal Army Medical Corps[1] described the typical Chindit as having "long hair, good manners, and exceptional intelligence".

They were a distinctive group, squatting cross-legged on their beds passing cigarettes from hand to hand after a single puff.

The most frequent clinical state was a combination of weight loss, chronic diarrhoea, and glossitis. Of the 191 men who knew their pre-expedition weight, the average loss in weight was 8.6 kg, but losses of 13 kg or more were common. Although much of the diarrhoea could be attributed to bacillary or amoebic dysentery, many cases remained unexplained and appeared to be the result of malabsorption of unknown etiology.

The loss in weight could be partly explained by diarrhoea and malabsorption but what we called "K-Ration anorexia" was a major factor. During their period behind the Japanese lines, food was supplied largely by air drop and had to be compact and light in weight. The basis of the Chindit diet was the American "K-Ration", a carefully balanced mixture of foods designed to appeal to the American palate, and intended for use only for short periods or emergencies. The energy content was 3200 kilocalories (13440 kJ) per day, and protein 100g; there was a slightly suboptimal daily intake of vitamin A (1450 I.U's), thiamin (1.5 mg), niacin (15 mg), riboflavin (2.1 mg) and ascorbic acid (60mg). This was approximately 1000 kilocalories (4200 kJ) short of what was required for strenuous physical exercise. In addition the Chindits complained that the whole ration tasted of spearmint and many of the men felt unable to consume it all because of the taste and the monotony. A typical "Supper" contained:

2 packets of biscuits (Energy Crackers)
1 tin of meat
1 envelope of bouillon powder
1 chocolate bar
1 packet of chewing gum
1 packet of cigarettes
1 packet of toilet paper

The glossitis was of the type seen in niacin deficiency, though there were a few cases of angular stomatitis, probably due to a deficiency of riboflavin. A number of men developed glossitis after admission to hospital, presumably because the high energy, high carbohydrate (4000 kilocalories, 8400 kJ) diet which they were given in hospital produced a relative imbalance between carbohydrate intake and depleted stores of niacin.

Some of the men had developed polyneuritis, loss of accommodation, and facial and palatal paralysis. There was one fatal case of respiratory paralysis which occurred after evacuation to a base hospital. We considered that a diphtheritic infection of "jungle sores", which were extremely common on the shins and lower leg, was responsible for these symptoms, though we were able to culture the diphtheria organism in only one case. A typical case history was as follows:

"Private.....,, admitted with a primary diagnosis of amoebic dysentery, he had had diarrhoea for four months, and a sore tongue for one month; he also complained of flatulence and heartburn. He had a unilateral facial palsy, weakness of the legs and paralysis of accommodation. His tongue was atrophic, red, and fissured. He had "jungle sores" on both legs, but no pathogens were isolated on culture."

There were eighty seven cases of infective hepatitis (hepatitis A) and three cases of serologically proved Weil's disease. There were six cases of scrub typhus, with one death (referred to above). A notable feature was the rarity of psychiatric casualties, 0.7%, compared to the 6% of patients admitted to 38 B.G.H. when in India.[1]

The reason why the Chindits were supplied with such an inadequate ration for so long remains unexplained; it was in any case a major error in planning which was subsequently corrected. Bernard Fergusson[2] in his book "The Wild Green Earth" stated that Wingate had insisted on the "K-Rations"; Wingate was never interested in the medical welfare of the soldiers under his command and regarded illness as a sign of weakness.

REFERENCES
1. Morris J N. Report on the health of 401 Chindits. Journal of the Royal Army Medical Corps 1945; 85: 123-32.
2. Fergusson B. The wild green earth. Cassells: 1956. 190.

III

A chance meeting in Calcutta –
Teaching army medicine in Poona –
Visit to the battle zone -Dacca (Dhaka)

IN SEPTEMBER 1944 I was posted from Assam to Poona in Western India as instructor at the Army Medical Training Centre (India) (A.M.T.C.(I)). It was apparently felt that I was too young to become a graded physician (a junior medical specialist) and that my talents would be wasted as a unit medical officer.

Our hospital jeep, with its dashboard instructions in Russian, deposited me at Golaghat station, to be informed by the station-master that the train was eight hours late. In due course I reached Gauhati, where I boarded the steamer for Serajgonj. At Serajgonj the train for Calcutta was waiting. Having settled myself in my compartment I suddenly realised that I had left the mess radio, which Jerry Morris had asked me to sell in Calcutta, on the deck of the steamer. I got hold of the nearest coolie, a sad looking albino with a distressingly scaly skin, and asked him to retrieve the set. A few stations down the line I was joined by two Chinese colonels on their way to a course in India. One of them had been in the Provincial Health Commission in Kweichow and gave me his card (plate 3). We shared my bully beef and army biscuits on the tedious journey to Calcutta. At Sealdah station I set out for the Officers' Hostel in the Grand Hotel (now the Oberoi Grand) in Chowringhee, choosing by some curious whim, a horse-drawn gharry, much to the disapproval of the porter and the surprise of the driver: a British officer should have taken a taxi. As we clip-clopped slowly through Calcutta a staff car whizzed past containing an officer with a red hatband whom I recognised as a friend, Tim (A.F.) Hely, now a brigadier in the artillery. Hely, a school dentist in peacetime, and

16

K. F. YAO

Provincial Health Commisson

Kweiyang, Kweichow

Plate 3
*Visiting card of a Chinese Colonel; the rail journey from Sirajgonj to
Calcutta, September 1944.*

a keen Territorial, had served in Palestine, Crete, the Western
Desert and for a brief period on the North West Frontier. In 1943
he was promoted to C.R.A. (Commander, Royal Artillery) in the
Seventh Indian Division which was operating on the Kohima-
Imphal front on the Assam-Burma border. His division was surrounded by the Japanese in the "Sinzweye Box" which was blocking
their advance into India. After a battle of sixteen days the Japanese
retreated for the first time in the war; this battle was a turning point
in the campaign. It must have been shortly after this that I saw him
in the staff car. I asked the porter at the "Grand" where a Brigadier
would be staying, "At the Bengal Club, Sahib", he said. I picked
up the telephone, got through to the Bengal Club, and asked for
Brigadier Hely, who invited me to dinner with his brigade major,
"Bulgy" Leach. I felt scruffy in my travel-stained "jungle greens"
in comparison with their spotless khaki drill, but we had an excellent meal. Having sold the radio the next thing was to get on a train
to Poona. The train conductor told me there were no vacant berths
but changed his mind when I gave him five "chips" (rupees).

Having organised my berth I had time for tea before we departed.
As we left Howrah station the waiter appeared to take my tray and
stepped elegantly off the moving train with the tray balanced on
the flat of his hand.

17

After the usual tedious journey I arrived at the AMTC(I) at Ganeshkind, a few miles outside Poona. I presented myself at the adjutant, Captain John Garlick, who asked me if I had a pleasant journey. I told him "Not really, it has taken me four days". "Oh", he said, "we thought you were in Bangalore".

The training centre was built in the form of a rectangle, with offices at one side and our living quarters on the other, and a parade ground in between. The functions of the centre was to give a basic training in army organisation, drill and military medicine to Indian officers who had just joined the I.A.M.C. (Indian Army Medical Corps). There was also a V.C.O. (Viceroy Commissioned Officer) section under the command of Major Frank Lake,* originally a medical missionary in India. One of their star accomplishments was the technique of carrying a loaded stretcher over a stone wall: there were no stone walls in Burma.

The instructors were an odd mixtur; the non-medical instructors were from various infantry regiments; two had a M.C. and had been posted to Poona presumably as some sort of reward; some of the others could have been got rid of by their units. In charge of the sepoys, who staffed the centre, were three majors. "Ratters" Ratcliffe and Edward Samson-Way were from the Gurkha Rifles, and Major Bhatia, from the Frontier Force Rifles, was a high-caste Brahmin who was so high caste that he scarcely spoke to anyone. "Ratters" had been a coffee planter in South India and lived with his family in Poona. Edward Samson-Way lived at the centre, and was looked after by a Gurkha orderly who lived with his rosy-cheeked wife in the compound.

The task of the medical instructors was to give lectures on medicine and surgery and to conduct an examination at the end of each course. The British medical instructors, apart from myself, were all Edinburgh graduates. Ian Veitch had been a G.P. in Galashiels, Douglas Frew from Kirkcaldy, was a trainee gynaecologist, and Paddy Bruce Lockhart was a trainee surgeon from Sedbergh. The British instructors were given nicknames by the sepoys. I was relieved to find that mine was "Jawan Sahib" (young sahib); Alec Sorrell, one of the military instructors, was "Chota Mota Sahib (little fat sahib). There were two Indian medical instructors,

---

* Later Director, Medical Theology College, Nottingham.

18

Captain Sharma from Lahore, and Captain Ramchandra. Ramchandra, who had a delightful sense of humour, came from the British-Indian 36th Division and told us he had marched 1300 km through Burma with Stilwell's Chinese forces. He had been gynaecologist to the Nizam of Hyderabad, a busy job as the Nizam had numerous wives. The Nizam, who was enormously rich, paid Ramchandra a pittance which was secretly made up by his wives. Ramchandra and I were the only instructors who had been east of the Bramahputra.

Our Commanding Officer was Colonel Basu, a kindly and dignified man, previously an ophthalmologist with the Indian Medical Service. He lived near the centre, and each year gave a party where the highlight was his wife's party trick in which she sat on the floor and peeled a potato into a chain of slices. Though it sounds extremely naive, it was a culture shock to be commanded by an Indian, my previous encounters with Indians had been at school where they were considered as honorary Englishmen, especially if they were good at games.

The intake of Indian officers was of variable quality; graduates from Bombay, Calcutta and Madras (Chennai) were uniformly excellent, but those from the medical colleges were not as good. For some reason, women were not sent on the course.

The work was not demanding; there was a tennis court, and Edward Samson-Way arranged for us to have riding lessons on clumsy cavalry horses with S.A. (Southern Army) branded on their flanks. A more unusual entertainment was to watch the centre's pet python being fed a live chicken. The chicken was put into the cage; nothing happened for a few minutes, then in an instant the chicken was in the snake's coils, being squeezed to death. The chicken was then swallowed whole, the bulge slowly travelling along to the snake's stomach. How or why a python was there I never found out; presumably it existed "on the strength" under the name of some fictitious sepoy. On another occasional a dead leopard was brought to the unit; it had been shot because it was killing livestock in the neighbouring villages; it was a beautiful animal. Apart from these local entertainments, the Poona Club had an excellent library, a swimming pool and squash courts. I managed to borrow a squash racket and arranged a game with the Indian "marker" (professional); he was much too good for me. Seeing him play in bare feet,

I decided to follow suit, but at the end of the match the soles of my feet were one continuous blister.

Everyone seemed to pass through Poona. While doing some lengths in the swimming pool I noticed an unusually large bow-wave approaching. As we met in the middle of the pool, the owner of the bow-wave said, "Black"; "Bentley" I replied. We met later for a beer and I was pleased to find that he was only a captain, like myself, despite reaching the unprecedented rank of under-officer in the School O.T.C. (Officers' Training Corps) at Haileybury. He subsequently returned to Haileybury as a master. I also met a couple, the husband now an instructor in the Royal Signals, whose marriage I had attended in 1937 in Wimbledon. Some R.A.M.C. officers clearly took to life in Poona; the Consultant Neurologist to Southern Army used to drive smartly round Poona in a pony trap.

One of the most interesting characters at the A.M.T.C. was my bearer, Merriman. An old man, who wore grubby cotton trousers and jacket, with a whiteish cloth wound round his head, he told me proudly, "I have Scotch blood", presumably this accounted for his unusual name, though he had a very dark skin. He also claimed to have been "Winston Churchill's dog-boy". Churchill was posted to the 4th Hussars in Bangalore in 1896 and he certainly had a terrier called "Winston". Though he had two "dressing boys", grooms for his horses, four washermen (dhobies) and a watchman, there is no mention in any of the numerous biographies of a "dog boy", but he may have been too unimportant to mention. Assuming Merriman was 65 years old in 1944 he would have been 17 in 1896, so his story was probably correct.

One of our duties was to be on the rota as orderly medical officer, to cope with any medical contingencies. On one of these days on duty I was called to see an Indian medical officer complaining of a pain in his chest. I managed to find my stethoscope and applied it to his chest. To my horror I could hear nothing. I wasn't deaf, and the officer was clearly alive, and I reassured him that there was nothing seriously wrong. So, had I completely lost the art of auscultation? I rushed back to my room and examined the earpieces of my stethoscope, they were neatly sealed off with a plug of dried mud; inside the mud were fat grubs, one on each side, presumably the offspring of a solitary wasp.

Though the work at the A.M.T.C. obviously lacked clinical experience this was offset by the extraordinary variety of material demonstrated in clinical meetings at the various hospitals in and around Poona. In addition to British and Indian troops there were large contingents of East and West Africans, and close to the A.M.T.C. were a large I.M.H. (Indian Military Hospital) and a civilian hospital. At the clinical meetings we saw all sorts of tropical disease: leprosy, Madura foot, Guinea worm, and cysticercosis. At the I.M.H. Lieutenant Colonel John Walters* took me round the wards with his graded physician, Captain Frezal. With Frezal I visited the civilian hospital. On one visit we came to a man, obviously very ill, with a high temperature, with a diagnosis of "P.U.O." (pyrexia of unknown origin). Frezal took one look at him, pulled back the sheets and showed me a large inguinal bubo (lymph gland), typical of plague. In the same ward was another patient with plague meningitis, a rare complication.

In November 1944 I went on leave to "Ooty" (Ootacamund) in the Nilgiris (Blue Hills) in South India. This involved a long train journey, followed by a four and a half hour climb up to the little town on the rack-and-pinion railway from Mettupalayam. Ooty, at an altitude of 2268 metres, was already a hill-station in the early 19th century and was used as a refuge from the heat of the plains by the Madras Government. Its Indianised Gothic Church of St Stephen was built in 1830; the churchyard was a sad place; the tombstones recorded the deaths of British children and of men and women dying in their early forties. I stayed at Rattan Tata Officers' Hostel, sharing a room with a lieutenant who had nightmares about his experiences in Burma and was consumed with guilt at having an affair with the wife of an officer who was on active service. There was golf, tennis, snooker, and picnics in the beautiful countryside, similar to the South Downs. There was also a wonderful smell of pines and eucalyptus; it was cold at night and we had log fires in the hostel.

I returned by way of Mysore, where I visited the Maharajah's palace, an Indo-Saracenic (a compromise style of architecture designed to please both Hindus and Muslims) extravaganza built in 1911-12.

---

* Later Consultant Physician, The Hospital for Tropical Diseases, London.

21

On Christmas Day we had some beers in the sergeant's mess and sang some of the old favourites, such as "My old man's a fireman in the Elder Dempster Line", and "Tora cheni, tora char, Bombay bibi bahut accha". (A little sugar, a little tea, Bombay girl [prostitute in this context] very good). After this and a large meal I decided to have a sleep. I was woken by Merriman, who sensing that my resistance would be low, asked me for five rupees for a "puja" (festival). Shortly after this we had a mess night at which Colonel Basu appeared in his blue and red uniform, confusingly called "mess dress, undress". At the end of the meal the I.A.M.C. pipers marched through the mess.

One of the perks of working at the A.M.T.C. was a visit to the 14th Army to assess the performance of ex-students. I was accompanied on most of the five week tour by Frank Lake. While waiting for a flight into Burma we visited a civilian kala-azar hospital on the outskirts of Calcutta. Hardly a hospital, it was a miserable shack, with rows of emaciated patients receiving inadequate treatment.

On April 19th we flew in a Dakota from Dum Dum airfield in Calcutta to Meiktila, stopping at Comilla and Monywa on the way. At the visitors' camp we found Brigadier 'Dick' Bomford,* Consultant Physician to the 14th Army. A friendly and amusing man, he had brought his accordion , which accompanied him on all his travels. I was interested to see that multivite tablets (thiamin, niacin, riboflavin and ascorbic acid) were distributed, along with mepacrine, for daily consumption. By the side of Meiktila Lake were two I.C.C.S.'s (Indian Casualty Clearing Stations) with mobile x-ray units and a shared operating tent. On the same site were a Chest Injury Unit, an Ophthalmic Unit and a Field Laboratory. Malaria was no longer a major problem in the area, mass spraying with D.D.T. from the air had almost eradicated mosquitoes.

Evacuation of casualties from field ambulances was by the little L5 monoplanes for sitting or lying cases. A L5 only required 300 yards for take-off. On May 1st we reported to 'M' (Medical) Branch H.Q.14th Army at Meiktila and were given air passages to Toungoo. These were cancelled because of heavy rain, the monsoon having started two weeks early. Instead we were attached to 64 Field

---

* Consultant Physician, The London Hospital.

Plate 4
Crossing the Sittang River, Burma, with 64 Field Company. Madras Sappers and Miners, May 5th, 1945.

Company, Madras Sappers and Miners, and arrived at Pyinmana where we spent two days watching elephants skilfully placing teak logs to build a bridge across the Sittang River and consuming wonderful curries with chapattis cooked on a spade over an open fire. In this unit all the officers, apart from the medical officer, who was an Indian, were British which placed him in an awkward position, socially and culturally. On May 6th we arrived at Toungoo, the H.Q. of the 19th Indian Division, where we were invited to attend the morning briefing session ("morning prayers") by Major General Pete Rees, a cheerful and confident man who always wore a red silk neckerchief. At Toungoo also, there was a small cage containing a half-dozen "Comfort girls" for the Japanese troops; it later transpired that the women were Korean, not Japanese. After visiting a number of Field Ambulances and C.C.S.s in the area we lodged with 13 I.C.C.S at Pegu, where I assisted the surgical specialist when he operated on some civilian casualties. It was here that I saw flame throwers; I was, perhaps naively, shocked at this, having assumed flame-throwers to be an exclusively German weapon.

I visited a large number of units in the Toungoo and Pegu area. On my way to a R.A.P. (Regimental Aid Post) I passed a rough notice with a skull and crossbones, and "14th Army rubbernecker"; presumably a victim of a landmine or a sniper. At this stage our food supply was entirely by "air drop" with hundreds of brightly coloured parachutes floating down from the sky. My final trip was from Pegu to Rangoon (Yangon) in a Bedford truck. The passage of tanks and other tracked vehicles had converted the road into a series of transverse ridges, making progress extremely uncomfortable, especially in a truck with "hard springing". It was evening and beginning to become cool as we approached Rangoon and every few yards there were snakes warming themselves on what remained of the tarmac surface of the road. Having arrived at Mingalodon, the airport for Rangoon, I felt sufficiently confident to apply the "perversity principle" and insisted that I must return to Calcutta by air. The result was a comfortable journey by hospital ship. At Calcutta I managed to get onto a hospital train to Poona. Fortunately there were no seriously ill patients on the train, since the medical equipment consisted of some Kramer wire and a few basic drugs, such as mepacrine and sulphaguanidine. I arrived back in Poona on May 31st, having been away for five weeks.

The object of this tour of 14th Army had been to obtain an impression of the work of the I.A.M.C. officers, more particularly those who had passed through the A.M.T.C. The general opinion was not encouraging. In general the Indians did not do well as regimental medical officers, though some were excellent. Most of the senior doctors felt that I.A.M.C. junior officers should work under supervision at units behind the lines.

On my return to Poona, I found a new officer had arrived. "Smithy" (I never discovered his first name), had been a lecturer in anatomy in Glasgow. Before being posted to India, Smithy had been the Medical Officer to a Guards unit; the peak of his Guards cap came down over his eyes, so that one could only see the lower part of his face and a bushy moustache. Smithy was a great asset in the mess; he had a bawdy sense of humour, and introduced us to some new phrases – "Rare as rocking horse shit", and "Eyes like pissholes in the snow". He gave us a brilliant lecture on the embryology and anatomy of the vertebral column. I heard later that he was invalided home with sprue; a friend who had been at his medical board for repatriation to the U.K. said "there was almost nothing left of him apart from his Guard's cap".

After 6 months at Poona I began to feel sidelined, and was anxious to return to more active service. When I saw one of the British instructors having his boots pulled off by his bearer, I knew it was time to leave. I wrote to Jerry Morris in Assam to see if he could help. My letter must have coincided with a visit to the A.M.T.C. of Brigadier Robert Platt,* Consultant Physician, India Command, who was complimentary about my lecture hand-outs and wrote to Jerry Morris about me. In July 1945 I was posted to 62 I.G.H. (C) (Indian General Hospital (Combined))** in Dacca as graded physician. The Commanding Officer was an eccentric Irishman, previously in the Indian Medical Service. When my turn came to be Orderly Officer, I accompanied him on an inspection of the latrines. Suddenly he turned to me and said, in his thick Cork accent, "Black, have you ever seen flies come out of a fellow's arse?". "No, Sir", I replied. "Well, they do, you know", he said, and we continued to the next latrine. I looked it up afterwards, and he was quite right; there are certain flies which can develop from grubs in the human intestinal tract.

The Colonel thought, probably rightly, that we were all very unfit and would benefit from some exercise. I was detailed off to take the British Other Ranks (B.O.R.'s) on a "route march". He probably thought I would make a mess of it; but remembering my drill from the O.T.C. I formed them up in three ranks in front of his office and marched them smartly off. When we were well away from the hospital compound I gave the order to "fall out" and everyone sat down by the roadside and had a smoke for fifteen minutes. We then formed up again and marched back.

One of my duties was to conduct an out-patient clinic. One day I was presented with an Sikh soldier with the lateral part of the bulbar conjunctiva of one eye covered with a greyish-yellow membrane; he had healed "jungle sores" on his shins, and I made a tentative diagnosis of diphtheritic conjunctivitis and sent him immediately to see an ophthalmologist, who confirmed the diagnosis.

---

* Later President of the Royal College of Physicians, London.
** "Combined" indicated a hospital staffed by British and Indian personnel, and taking both Indian and British patients.

IV

News of the atom bomb – Singapore and the prisoners of war

ON AUGUST 6th 1945 I hitched a lift on a Dakota taking casualties from Dacca to Calcutta. Over the Bay of Bengal the pilot picked up the news that the Americans had dropped an atom bomb on Hiroshima. I was distracted from taking in the implications of this astonishing information by the struggles of a large West African soldier, on his way to a psychiatric unit, to free himself from a stretcher to which he was firmly strapped. Because of the heat the plane was flying with one of its loading doors open, and the stretcher was alarmingly near this open space.

I spent a week in Calcutta on a temporary posting and was able to celebrate August 14th – VJ Day – with Lieutenant Colonel Sheehan (the O.C. Medical Division of my late hospital in Dacca) and a lot of gin at Firpo's restaurant in Calcutta. (VE Day, May 8th 1945, passed without comment in India and South East Asia; we all anticipated a prolonged war with Japan). Colonel Sheehan was on his way home and gave me Stitt's two volumes on "Diagnosis, Prevention and Treatment of Tropical Diseases" which I still have. I spent the night of August 14th sharing a room at the "Grand", the officers' transit hostel, with two lieutenants from an Indian infantry regiment and their black labrador. Though at the beginning of their leave, they were already feeling the separation from their "Jawans" (a familiar term for an Indian soldier, or sepoy; literally a "youth") and I began to appreciate the strength of the bond, a sort of father and son relationship, between the British officer and his sepoys, which was one of the best traditions of the Indian Army.

26

The next day I joined 47 B.G.H. which was embarking on the hospital ship 'H.S. Karoa', in the docks on the Hooghly river. The 'Karoa' was part of "Operation Zipper", originally intended as a seaborne force for the invasion of Singapore. We had to wait until the Japanese commander in Singapore, General Igataki of the 7th Area Army, decided to obey the Emperor's instructions to surrender, and spent the time swinging on our anchor in the middle of the Bay of Bengal, playing table tennis and listening to Bing Crosbie's "Beautiful Dreamer" on someone's gramophone. We docked in Singapore on September 7th, 5 days after the Japanese surrender; the formal surrender took place in the presence of Lord Mountbatten, the Supreme Commander, South East Asia, on September 12th, but I was too busy in the hospital to go to see it. On the quayside were hundreds of emaciated men, strolling around, chatting in groups, or sitting on the bollards. Some were wearing tattered remnants of uniform, some ragged shorts and others only a "G-string". Packets of cigarettes thrown onto the quay were

Plate 5
The surrender of the Japanese Army, Singapore, September 12th,
1945.

eagerly grabbed and distributed, each man taking a single puff and handing it on to his neighbour.

We took over the Alexandra Hospital, the largest general hospital in Singapore, which had been used by the Japanese Army. The first thing we noticed was a peculiar sweet-sour smell which we hopefully attributed to Japanese food. Everywhere were signs of a hasty departure; in the offices photographs of wives and girlfriends were still pinned on the walls, and on the tables were cigarette ends and matchboxes decorated with vicious caricatures of Churchill and Roosevelt. In one office there was a huge Japanese script typewriter.

The hospital was very dirty and most of the equipment was out of order. Blankets and mattresses had to be disinfested or destroyed. The pharmacy contained, apart from the usual drugs, exotic preparations such as "Bear's Foot Ointment" (labelled in English and Japanese), whose purpose I have never discovered. The Japanese had catalogued the hospital medical library and had added some of their own texts. While I was there a gaunt figure came in, his clothes hanging off him, and put a book on one of the shelves; he explained that he had borrowed it in 1942.

When Singapore fell 50,000 British, Australian and Indian troops and civilians were taken prisoner. When the Japanese capitulated there were 9,000 British, 6,000 Australian and 1,500 Indian troops on the island. Three thousand British troops were in Changi gaol, built to house six hundred. In August 1945 there were 4,500 civilians (including 328 children) interned in Singapore. Most of the military personnel originally in Singapore had been dispersed to various labour camps such as those for building the Burma-Siam ("River Kwai") railway. It has been estimated that one third of those taken prisoner died from malnutrition, disease or ill-treatment; this compares with the figure of one in twenty for German and Italian prisoners of war camps.

In the few days after we arrived, when the number of admissions was relatively small, we had time to explore Singapore. We hired an ancient Austin 10 and careered round Singapore getting lost frequently because the English street names had been taken down and the Chinese seemed to have forgotten any English they had once known. We developed a curious euphoria which manifested itself in stupid and irresponsible behaviour and a "bolshie" attitude to authority. We invaded the Tiger Balm Gardens* and broke bits off the plaster animals and plants as souvenirs; later I felt ashamed and threw my bits away. Wild rumours circulated, one was that there were bodies buried in the hospital grounds. A digging party was formed, but when I directed them to a smelly area they found only a dump of bad bananas.

On September 9th, two days after our arrival, we began to admit patients; during the next four days we admitted 20 patients daily, mainly from the Changi gaol hospital. It was just as well that the admissions were so few because the 'Karoa' had only brought the minimum equipment and stores for 200 beds; the "back up" stores did not arrive until 6 weeks later. Though the hospital x-ray equipment was soon repaired we found that the films we had brought from India were mostly fogged and unusable. The 'Karoa' brought 50 nursing sisters but by October 1st at the peak of our admissions we had a hundred.

On October 1st we admitted 320 patients and three weeks later 270. There were now 1,150 beds occupied, 1,000 by released allied prisoners of war and internees – "RAPWI" as they were called – and 150 "local sick". The patients were now coming by ship and air, from Borneo, Sarawak, Java, Sumatra and Bangkok; all were too ill to be evacuated by hospital ship to India. Most of the men were British, Australian or Indian servicemen (Indian troops were admitted to another hospital in Singapore), with some from the Royal Dutch Army and a few civilians; less than 2% of the patients were women, the majority of the women and children having been evacuated before Singapore fell on February 25th 1942. It was at this stage that we received a visit from Lieutenant Colonel G A Ransome, a controversial figure who had escaped from Singapore and because of this had been severely criticised by his medical colleagues who had remained behind.

"Operation Zipper" had been planned for an invasion, and the only food available for the patients at the beginning were K-Rations (see p.14), Pacific Tinned Rations (Meat and Vegetable Stew ("M & V") and Steak and Kidney Pudding), quite unsuitable for men whose diet had consisted mainly of rice for the past three and a half

---

* A garden containing plaster animals and plants, built by the millionaire manufacturer of "Tiger Balm" liniment and various herbal remedies.

years. By September 12th Australian Red Cross supplies arrived and we were able to give a graduated semi-solid diet to the more severely ill patients. After being in action for two weeks we began to run short of vitamin preparations and were forced to use Japanese thiamin (B1) tablets containing 0.3 mg and ampoules of 1.0 mg; this necessitated using large numbers of tablets and ampoules to achieve the necessary high dosage for the treatment of beri-beri.

The following clinical description is based on a report prepared by J B Mitchell (at that time one of the medical specialists at 47 B.G.H.) and myself.[1]

Each patient, when admitted to hospital was clutching a small bag or a battered tin containing the few personal items he had managed to keep during the years of captivity. At first they insisted on keeping these under their pillows and it was only later that we were able to persuade them that it was safe to put them in their bedside locker.

During their captivity, men, including those who were not desperately ill, were forced to undertake hard manual work. The energy content of their diet rarely exceeded 2000 kilocalories (8400 KJ) and in August 1945 it was reduced in some camps to 1500 kilocalories (6800 KJ). Men who were too sick to work received a smaller ration. The diet was grossly deficient in protein, fat and the B group of vitamins, and probably to a lesser extent in vitamin A. Excluding those with oedema, the average loss in weight during captivity was between 16 and 18 kg. Many of the severely ill patients were extremely apathetic with no desire to eat or even to live: obtaining a history was a very slow process. Apart from severe emaciation 50% of the patients were suffering from combinations of clinical thiamin, riboflavin and niacin deficiencies. A quarter of the men had oedema of varying degree, due to hypoproteinaemia and thiamin deficiency. There were a few cases of gross oedema, with effusions into the serous cavities and breathlessness, which were due to "wet" or cardiac beri-beri. However most of the patients with beri-beri had the "dry" or polyneuritic form, with muscular weakness and wasting, ataxia, loss of distal sensation, and absent tendon reflexes. This was quite different from the isolated nerve palsies usually seen in diphtheria; diphtheritic infection of the fauces and tropical ulcers had occurred in the camp between 1942 and 1944.[2] Magenta tongue, cheilosis, angular stomatitis and scrotal dermatitis were the main manifestations of riboflavin

30

deficiency while niacin deficiency was indicated by a sore tongue, with reddened papillae at the edges and tip. The pigmented skin of pellagra was rare but nearly all patients had a thin scaly skin. Scabies, without the typical skin lesions, was common, as I discovered when my forearms began to itch at night. Diarrhoea was such a common symptom and had so many possible causes, often in the same patient, that it was not possible to say whether this was part of the pellagra syndrome. Burning feet ("Happy Feet") was a frequent complaint and is thought to be due to a deficiency of pantothenic acid. Among the conditions whose aetiology was uncertain were amblyopia with partial optic atrophy and central or paracentral scotomata, and petechiae on the forearms, shoulders and lower legs; the latter appeared suddenly and lasted for 1-2 weeks; there did not appear to be any response to ascorbic acid. Diet consisted initially of condensed milk, beaten-up eggs and sugar, supplemented later by protein hydrolysate; the hydrolysate was not liked because of its unpleasant taste so it was perhaps just as well that it only became available about a week after we started admitting patients, having been at the bottom of a hold in a freighter. All patients were given compound vitamin tablets daily, mepacrine as a malaria suppressant and "Marmite" or "Vegemite" as desired. For those whose diarrhoea did not improve within 2-3 days of dietary treatment we gave a course of sulphaguanidine. Riboflavin was not available other than in the vitamin tablets, but niacin was given to those with evidence of pellagra or glossitis. "Dry" beri-beri was treated with oral or intramuscular thiamin, and "wet" beri-beri with thiamin intravenously. The response to treatment was usually rapid, with an improvement in mental state and a gain in weight of about 2.4 kg in a week. Polyneuritic beri-beri improved rather slowly. Worrying features were adverse effects of treatment. A too rapid increase in food intake caused circulatory collapse, possibly due to a dumping syndrome. One patient who became ill and collapsed for no obvious reason was found to have large quantities of noodles in his locker, having persuaded the Chinese ward orderly to buy them in the city. Sudden unexpected death occurred in a few cases and we heard of similar deaths in Singapore, in non-hospital patients, generally after a large meal. This was attributed to an acute deficiency of thiamin precipitated by a large intake of carbohydrate. In a few cases tongue lesions appeared or became worse after admission, and in one or two instances ataxia appeared which had not been present previously.

31

In all such cases it appeared to be the increased intake of carbo-hydrate or possibly of protein which had exacerbated a pre-existing deficiency in spite of our treatment. The most distressing complication of treatment, for resistant oedema, was the development of pulmonary oedema during an infusion of double strength plasma, though this was given very slowly, at the rate of one pint over twelve hours. Though we were aware of the danger of hyper-volaemia we had not fully appreciated the necessity of inducing a simultaneous diuresis, nor the degree of myocardial damage produced by prolonged malnutrition and thiamin deficiency. Of three cases with this complication, two died. Of the 1,230 patients admitted between September 9th and November 30th there were 21 deaths, eight (including those due to plasma infusions) were attributable to malnutrition and beri-beri; four died from pul-monary tuberculosis; the remainder were due to a variety of causes not related to captivity. It was unfortunate that our pathologist decided not to keep any of the tissues for histology, thus wasting some unique material. The following two cases illustrate some of the problems encountered.

Case 1. Male, aged 21 years, sergeant in the Royal Dutch Army. (see Fig 1). He was admitted to 47 B.G.H. on September 10th from Changi gaol hospital where he had been since November 1944 with the diagnosis of chronic diarrhoea, severe anaemia, beri-beri and malaria. He had a history of amoebic dysentery in 1938 and in 1942 a diagnosis of sprue had been made; during 1945 he had numerous attacks of malaria. On admission to Changi he had a Hb of 6.0g per 100 ml with a megalocytic blood picture; his stools con-tained giardia trophozoites. When he was admitted to 47 B.G.H. his Hb was 4.8 g per 100 ml with 0.2% reticulocytes. He was very pale and wasted, with a smooth pink tongue. However the most striking feature was an extreme apathy, with no desire to eat or to live.

On a ward round with the O.C. Medical Division (Lieutenant Colonel Robert Spicer)* and one of the medical specialists, they passed his bed with a shrug and no discussion, and it was clear that they had written him off. The St. Thomas' trained ward sister (she was later "mentioned in dispatches") and I were outraged and determined to prove them wrong. He was gradually persuaded to

---

* Later Consultant Physician to the British Army of the Rhine.

32

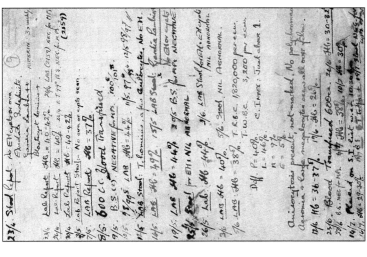

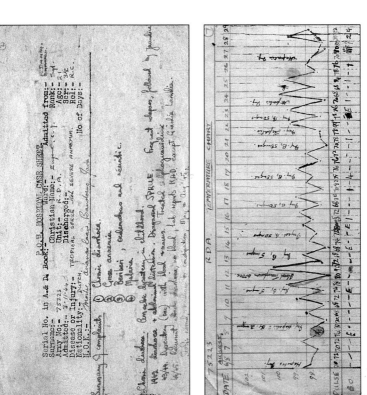

Figure 1
Part of the case sheet of a sergeant in the Royal Dutch Army while a patient in Changi Gaol Hospital.

33

eat and finally accepted liver extract and Marmite orally and a graduated diet. He was given three pints of blood, and injections of liver extract daily, in addition to sulphaguanidine and suppressive mepacrine. Gradually his morale improved and he gained weight, his reticulocyte count rose to 2.4% and his Hb increased from 7.8 to 12.2g per 100 ml without further transfusion. He was finally transferred at the beginning of November 1945 to a base hospital in India from which he sent me a photograph of himself, looking well nourished and cheerful.

Case 2. Male, civilian in the Malayan Medical Service. He had been in Outram Road Civil Prison between November 1944 and August 1945, and had been kept for a fortnight in a wooden box as a punishment for some minor misdemeanour. When admitted to 47 BGH his knees were hyperextended and could not be fully flexed. With physiotherapy he rapidly improved and was evacuated on a hospital ship to Madras, and then to a hospital in Bangalore. He later returned to Singapore where he remained until 1959.

By the end of September the number of new patients was down to about 50 a day: we still had 400 "RAPWI" and around 250 "local sick". It was at this stage that Robert Spicer, presumably intending to discipline me in some way for my anti-authority behaviour, discovered that one of my case sheets was incomplete and took it up to his room. Fearing some form of military punishment or demotion a friend and I decided to put things right. During the night we crept into Colonel Spicer's room with a shaded torch, removed the case sheet, which was on his bedside table, while he was asleep under his mosquito net, completed the case sheet and returned it to the bedside table. Next morning the case sheet reappeared and nothing was said. I subsequently came to appreciate his casual "throw-away" style and when we both returned to England he invited me to a tennis party at the Queen Elizabeth Military Hospital in Woolwich.

At the beginning of October a new disaster struck. Between October 4th and the 15th we admitted forty one cases of suspected methyl alcohol (methanol) poisoning. The "Straits Times" of October 12th reported that twenty servicemen had died; it was not known how many civilians were affected. It was thought that the methyl alcohol had been looted from stores left by the Japanese, or had been produced by illicit stills. The outbreak was due to the drinking of cheap wine or water coloured to resemble wine, brandy, or whisky, and adulterated with methyl alcohol. The alcohol must have been fairly pure and did not contain any additives such as fusel oil to discourage drinking. Typically, drinkers were less intoxicated on the day on which they drank than they would have expected, only to awake next morning with a hangover which became worse during the following twelve hours. Most cases were admitted between 36 hours and 48 hours after their drinking bout. Five patients were dead on arrival at the hospital, and five died soon after admission. On admission they were drowsy or in deep coma, flushed, with acidotic breathing, and widely dilated pupils. All cases had retinal oedema, with swelling of the disc which in the more severe cases progressed to optic atrophy. Treatment was by stomach wash-out, intravenous fluids and sodium bicarbonate orally; in a few cases two lumbar punctures were done with the object of removing as much methyl alcohol from the central nervous system as possible, but this did not seem to influence the outcome. Of the thirty six survivors, three had a slight visual defect, two were partially blind, and in two vision was reduced to the appreciation of hand movements. An unusual feature in one case was the development of peripheral neuritis on the sixth day after admission; six weeks later there was almost complete recovery. We were of course unable to follow up these cases, but it seemed unlikely that there would be significant improvement in vision in the two men most severely affected.

Methyl alcohol is broken down rather slowly into formic acid and small amounts of formaldehyde and it is formic acid which is thought to be mainly responsible for the acidosis and damage to the optic nerve. Both compounds are powerful reducing agents, which would account for the reduction of silver nitrate to metallic silver (a black deposit in the test tube) when we tested the patients' urine for chlorides, using the now outmoded Fantus' test.[*]

By a curious coincidence, a few months later I encountered another case of methyl alcohol poisoning in Malacca (Malaka). An

---

[*] A test for estimating the chloride content of urine in which 1 drop of 20% potassium chromate is added to 10 drops of urine: a 2.9% solution of silver nitrate is added drop by drop until the colour changes from yellow to brown. The number of drops of silver nitrate required gives the number of grams per litre of sodium chloride.

Indian ward orderly who had been working in the laboratory was found in a deep coma, with stertorous breathing and widely dilated pupils. He died shortly after admission. We were able to confirm that he could have had access to methyl alcohol in the laboratory. Histology of an eye showed engorgement of the choroidal vessels and swelling of a few ganglion cells; in the nerve fibre layer the fibres were thickened, and separated by oedema.

Apart from the thrill of drinking at the famous long bar in Raffles Hotel my most pleasant memory was attending the first post-war performance of the Singapore Symphony Orchestra. This was a truly multi-ethnic occasion with Chinese, Europeans, Hindus, Malays and Sikhs all playing away enthusiastically. In December 1945 I was posted to 24 IGH (C) in Malacca.

REFERENCES
1. Mitchell J B, Black J A. Malnutrition in released prisoners of war and internees in Singapore. Lancet (2) 1946: 855-63.
2. Smith D A, Woodruff M F A. Deficiency diseases in Japanese prison camps. Medical Research Council Special Reports Series No 274. London: H.M.S.O.: 1951, 6.

V

Malaya after the war – Burma again – Return to a cold U.K.

THE HOSPITAL in Malacca was in a modern hospital building, formerly the district hospital. Malacca was, and still is, a sleepy little fishing town at the mouth of the Muar river. The hospital looked after military and civilian sick. I learned how to say "Breathe in and out" in Urdu, Tamil, Malay and Japanese.

The staff on the wards consisted of I.A.M.C. male orderlies, local Chinese nurses and British V.A.D.s (Voluntary Aid Detachment); each ward was in the charge of a British Nursing Sister. On my ward was an excellent Indian orderly, Lance Naik (Lance Corporal) Abdul Wali Khan, from a village near Peshawar, on the North West Frontier (now in Pakistan). A sturdy man, who was fond of the children, he wore unmilitary chupplies (sandals) instead of boots. One day he asked me if I would recommend him for promotion to naik (corporal), which I did. On the day his promotion came through he announced that we were to become "blood brothers" to which I agreed, feeling very flattered. The ceremony consisted of mixing our bloods, obtained by finger prick with a blood count lancet. Long after I had returned to England we corresponded. Wali Khan was then a "compounder" (a dispenser) in his village. In 1954 he offered to have some shoes made in his village, so I sent him the money and an outline of my bare feet; unfortunately the shoemaker assumed that the outline was of my shoe. The resulting shoes, though beautifully made, were a very tight fit, though I loyally squeezed my feet into them from time to time.

The majority of civilian cases were admitted for nutritional (famine) oedema or severe anaemia or a combination of both conditions. The oedema did not respond to parenteral thiamin and

37

Plate 6
A patient with a locally recruited nurse, 24 I.G.H. (C), Malacca,
Malaysia, December 1945.

there was a variable response to mersalyl. Total protein levels ranged from 4.5g to 7.2g per 100ml, with oedema present at levels of less than 5.8g per 100 ml. The anaemia was hypochromic and normocytic, due to a combination of iron deficiency, chronic malaria, and in many cases hookworm infestation. One patient had a Hb level of 1.5g per 100ml and five had levels between 3.0 and 4.0 per 100ml. Ascaris (roundworm) infestation was common either on its own or combined with hookworm. Fifteen per cent of the civilians developed an attack of benign tertian (vivax) malaria while in hospital and one patient had malignant tertian (falciparum) malaria.

Among other conditions in the civilian patients were two cases of secondary and one case of tertiary yaws with bone lesions. Yaws was endemic in the rural Malays and Chinese; secondary yaws caused severe facial disfigurement. There was one case of amoebic hepatitis and one case each of typhoid and paratyphoid C fevers.

Two patients were found to have pulmonary tuberculosis and one had abdominal tuberculosis. Among the military cases there were two cases of scrub typhus, one in a British officer who developed the unusual complication of myocarditis, with congestive cardiac failure, but made a complete recovery. Most unusually there were five cases of pericarditis; one appeared to be due to rheumatic fever and was treated with salicylates. The other four cases were tuberculous. Two of these had been prisoners of war, one in Germany, and one in Italy, who had escaped and managed to reach England via Switzerland and France, an astonishing feat for someone so obviously non-European.

Things did not always go according to plan. A small Tamil boy was admitted with severe hypochromic anaemia, due to iron deficiency and hookworm infestation. We decided to give him a blood transfusion in the evening and to let it run overnight. Next morning he was dead; the remaining blood in the bottle was a dark purplish red colour and was obviously infected. In the dim artificial light on the previous evening we had failed to see that the blood was an unusual colour, or the colour might have changed during the night.

We had some contact with the local Chinese community and some of us were invited to the wedding of the daughter of a local business man. This was a lavish affair, with wonderful Chinese food. I obtained permission to visit the court room in Malacca, and was amused to see that the lawyers wore striped shorts, their bare legs invisible behind their desks, of a pattern similar to the trousers worn by British lawyers. On one occasion I was asked to see a Chinese nun, in a nunnery near Malacca. She looked very thin and ill, and appeared, according to the x-ray, to have a partly healed tuberculous lesion. The nunnery smelled, like all such buildings, of floor polish. The Japanese had allowed the nuns to remain undisturbed during their occupation.

After I had been in Malacca for a few months, the C.O. returned to the U.K. and was replaced by Robert Spicer, who had been my O.C. Medical Division in Singapore. A welcome visitor was Brigadier Max Rosenheim,* now Consultant Physician to A.L.F.S.E.A. (Allied Land Forces, South East Asia). Max was his usual urbane and perceptive self, his chubby legs in shorts and long

---

* Later President of the Royal College of Physicians, London.

khaki socks. We knew each other well; he had been my tutor in medicine at U.C.H. (University College Hospital) when my year had been evacuated to Cardiff from 1939 to 1940.

Shortly after Max's visit I began to suffer from attacks of severe abdominal colic. I had little faith in the senior surgeon at the hospital and was anxious to find a non-surgical cause for my symptoms. Having read somewhere that abdominal colic was a symptom of ascariasis (though rarely described in the textbooks) I had a stool examined in the laboratory; this showed a heavy infestation with roundworms. A single dose of tetrachlorethylene made me feel slightly drunk and produced a large number of macerated worms. Since it takes about two months for the worms to reach adult size, I probably acquired them in one of the Chinese restaurants in Malacca.

Travel at this time was safe and easy, so safe that I threw my revolver into a pond, and on the advice of the quartermaster, recorded it as "lost in transit". Nevertheless there were signs that all was not as tranquil as it appeared. Force 136 were already hunting Chinese Communists in the jungle and rubber plantations but it was not until much later that the full-blown "Emergency" was declared.

In keeping with the euphoric atmosphere in the immediate postwar period someone in H.Q. 34 Indian Corps in Kuala Lumpur had the bright idea of circulating all medical units and unit medical officers with a spoof directive on "Throps". This purported to have come from H.Q. 14th Army S.E.A.C. (South East Asia Command) dated October 11th 1945. The following is an abridged version of the directive. I have left the original spelling unchanged to retain the "atmosphere".

"Subject: *Notification of Disease – Throps*
              Herewith a copy of an account of a Tropical Disease –
              Throps. Please be on the look out for the a/n disease
              and notify it's occurence to this H.Q., or A.F.A. – 35.
              Sgd..........................Brig.
              DDMS Fourteenth Army

Subject: *THROPS*
              Cases of Throps are beginning to recur in this area.
Throps, which is almost entirely restricted to the Southern half of

Burma, has not been seen since the retreat from Burma. At that time, there was a small epidemic amongst the Senegalese Labour Battalion working on the Hmawbi-Budalin Road. That the Japanese had many cases is made clear from Hanseatic documents which show that in the Shawlu Valley in one Butai alone there were no less than 123 cases.

Geographical Distribution:　　　Restricted to Burma and to a small district in Malaya, east of Kuala Lumpur.

Aetiology:　　　　　　　　The causative organism has never been isolated but is thought to be a rickettsia similar to that causing Proya Fever. This rickettsia has as its host the small "Eye-Fly" that dwells on Carrom Grass. Carrom Grass may be easily recognised by its typical feathery vectales. The route of infection from the Fly to the individual has never yet been satisfactorily established, but Soyagesa, working in Malaya in 1941 suggested it was through the hair follicles of the eyelids and eyebrows.

Morbid Pathology:　　　　At post mortem the only constant findings are those of severe toxaemia. However, Probyn (1943) reports widespread and minute haemorrhages in the Circular Gyrus similar to those found in Arnical's Encephalopathy.

Incubation Period:　　　　2-24 days.

Clinical Manifestations:　　　The first symptoms is a peculiarly severe reoerbital headache. This may continue for several days until the cerebral symptoms appear. These take the form of profound mental depression, so much so, that in this stage patients may commit suicide. At the same time the patient appears to suffer intero-lateral irritation of the bladder with consequent frequency of urine.

Clinically the most striking feature of this disease is the characteristic pose adopted by the patient – his head thrust forward and a pecular glitter in the eye. On Ophthalmoscopy, the disc appears blurred and the arteries and vein are indistinguishable. At or about the 6th day, when the irritation begins, there is a fine squamous rash on the trunk and eyelids.

The only certain diagnosis feature is the temperature, which may drop as low as 94.5 -95. In spite of this, the patient may feel warm and even throw off blankets.

Toxaemia increases and at the end of the third week the patient gradually succumbs.

Administration of standard pyretics may be of assistance.

41

Prophylaxis: Clearing of areas where there is Carrom Grass may prove too difficult but liberal spraying with DDT should be undertaken. Each individual in the area should be issued with a small container and if possible an individual sparklet.

Summary: Throps is again beginning to become a medical problems in S Burma. Isolation of the patient, and energetic countermeasures should be taken and noted on AFA 35."

I was now due for annual leave, which I took in the Cameron Highlands, a pleasantly cool hill station (1640 metres above sea level). I stayed at the Officers' Hostel, the former Cameron Highlands Hotel, built in the 1930's and overlooking a nine-hole golf course. We occasionally saw the aboriginal tribesmen, the Orang Asli, armed with their blow pipes for killing game. Apart from resuscitating my golf the only memorable occurrence was finding, one night, a caterpillar racing across the path, each segment having a ring of luminous hair tufts.

Plate 7
Japanese prisoner of war camp. Johor Bahru, Malaysia, 1946.

Shortly after this I was posted temporarily to a hospital in Johor Bahru, near the causeway linking the mainland with the island of Singapore. At low tide there were curious little fish which propelled themselves out of the water and on to the mud using their lateral fins. Robert Spicer reappeared as the C.O. of the hospital. By this time we were on friendly terms and he invited me and some others to the Officers' Club. We encountered a young Indian military policeman who courageously stopped our jeep, driven by a full colonel, and asked for our authorisation for the use of an Army vehicle for recreational purposes. Unfortunately, we had no such authorisation and the matter was reported to higher authority. Robert Spicer was demoted temporarily to lieutenant colonel. However he soon regained the "red tabs". After a few weeks in Johor I was posted to 52 I.G.H. (C) in the old Civil Hospital in Rangoon (I visited it 40 years later, as a patient, and it seemed completely unchanged). We found a complete set of cricket gear at the hospital and amused ourselves at the nets.

I was soon sent, as a graded physician, to a C.C.S. acting as a hospital at Prome on the banks of the Irrawaddy, in South Burma. Prome was a pleasant little town, with a central square and market place overlooked by a pagoda with steps leading up to it, guarded by two large Chindits, the mythical Burmese griffin, and the emblem of Wingate's Special Forces. Just outside the town was a soda water factory producing bottles with glass ball stoppers (Codd's bottles). The C.C.S. was on a small hill with a "flame of the forest" tree at its apex. The wards faced low jungle and behind was a flat plain. The C.O. was a charming and amusing Sikh, with a M.C. from the Italian campaign. In the evening we sat outside our huts drinking beer while he combed his long hair over the back of a chair. Most of the officers were British, though the radiologist, Captain Steiner, was an Austrian refugee who had previously been with Chiang Kai-Shek's Chinese forces in China. He had a low opinion of them, saying that they specialised in mock battles with the Japanese and in blowing up unimportant bridges. The graded surgeon was Anand Pardhy who had been resident surgical officer at Birmingham's Queen Elizabeth Hospital before joining the R.A.M.C. The dental officer was a Yorkshireman who copied out "Eskimo Nell" for me in red ink; to my great regret I lost this priceless manuscript. The quartermaster was a "regular", with a keen sense of humour. He showed me the instructions on the packing case of a piece of equipment, which read "The bottom shall be labelled top, to avoid confusion". At his repatriation party he got rather drunk and put mayonnaise on to the fruit salad.

About a mile from the C.C.S. was a camp of Japanese soldiers awaiting repatriation. They had their own medical officers and a dentist. The dental officer, with whom I became friendly, spoke good English and acted as liaison officer; he and the medical officers held the rank of sergeant, an indication of the low status afforded to the medical services in the Japanese Army. The camp provided working parties for tasks such as clearing railway embankments. Normally the Japanese looked after their own sick, but seriously ill medical cases and those requiring surgery were admitted to the C.C.S.

The admission of Japanese sick to a general ward containing Gurkha patients produced some problems. The Gurkhas wanted to chop the heads off the Japanese patients, and their kukris had to be removed when they were admitted. I explained that the war was over; my Burma Star seemed to convince them.

When we started to admit soldiers from the Japanese Camp with scrub typhus (a number of whom died) I discovered that they had been given no protection against typhus. There were two methods of protection, either by a vaccine which had recently become available, or by impregnating clothing with a mite repellent dibutylphthalate (D.B.P.) I complained to the British officer in charge of the working parties that it was his duty to keep the Japanese soldiers healthy and that in any case the high sickness rate was depleting his work force. Though they were not given the vaccine they were supplied with D.B.P. which was remarkably effective, as a list of typhus patients compiled by the senior medical officer in the camp showed. The staff of the C.C.S. had all been given the typhus vaccine, but we had one case in a nursing sister who had recently joined the unit; she had the typical eschar (the site of the mite attachment, with the appearance of a cigarette burn) on the back of her neck.

The Japanese had a very high incidence of malaria. After we introduced mepacrine there was a remarkable reduction in the number of cases, as shown by the graph (fig. 2).

There was little in the way of entertainment; we could take a Jeep down to the Irrawaddy to swim, and watch the rafts of teak logs, each with a little hut on it, as they floated down to the mouth

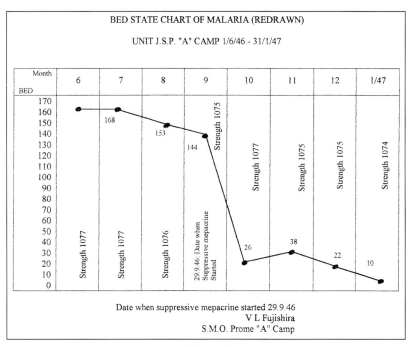

Figure 2
Graph of the incidence of malaria in the Japanese Prisoner of War Camp at Prome, Burma, showing the effect of the introduction of daily mepacrine tablets.

of the river. We had a few shows; the unit sepoys put on a programme of Indian dancing. They had no inhibitions in taking the female roles. The Japanese camp also put on a musical show, using instruments which they had ingeniously constructed from bamboo and tins. We were also entertained to a Burmese play by a troupe from the town. The play lasted three and a half hours and at the end of it I had worn a hole in the seat of my trousers, due to restless shifting on a wicker seated chair from boredom.

Apart from the play we had little contact with the Burmese though much of our food was purchased locally. On one occasion we were given some turtle's eggs, which looked like damaged ping-pong balls and tasted fishy. Burmese chickens, like Indian ones, were tough and skinny and required boiling before being roasted,

45

the result being known as "boily-roast chicken". Being a combined unit, there was a choice of Indian or British food. The Indian food was much better as the British food came mainly out of tins.

The ways of the Indian Army were a continual surprise. One day one of the nursing orderlies presented me with his pay-book and asked me to authorise his allowance of opium. The exact quantity was written in the back of the pay-book; this seemed a very sensible way of dealing with opium addiction.

Anand Pardhy had a .22 rifle with which he took pot shots at "pai" dogs and Benson and Hedges cigarette tins on sticks. The first and only time I used the rifle I received a blast of powder on to my right cornea. Anand always wore glasses and so had not noticed that the breech was defective. I was given atropine drops which dilated the pupil, making it very painful to go out in the full glare of the sun. It was obvious, from the continued pain that I had some powder stuck to my cornea, and I was quickly taken by truck to Rangoon where a Sikh ophthalmologist put fluorescein drops in my eye to confirm the presence of the foreign body; the contents of the bottle must have evaporated slightly because the fluorescein was intensely painful and was presumably hypertonic. However, the foreign body on my cornea was quickly removed, using a slit-lamp.

I had only two other contacts with the local population. I thought it would be nice to have a kitten, so I bought a small basket and a kitten was obtained from the town. Almost immediately it became ill with gastroenteritis and died. Another was produced; this seemed healthy enough but one night I awoke just in time to see a jungle cat making off into the jungle with my kitten in its mouth. After that I gave up.

My other contact with the people of Prome was even less happy. One morning a local doctor brought a Burmese woman to the C.C.S.; he said she was very anaemic and about twelve weeks pregnant. I confirmed her haemoglobin as being less than 4.5g per 100ml, with a megaloblastic blood film. Clearly she needed a transfusion. Her blood group was AB, not uncommon in South East Asia, and so by coincidence is mine. After cross-matching, I gave her a pint of my blood, and she returned home. I heard later that she had miscarried soon afterwards.

After I had been in Prome for a few weeks we began to admit a succession of Japanese soldiers with acute appendicitis. During the following six months we admitted a total of ten cases. During the same period there were no cases of appendicitis from any of the British, Indian, Gurkha, Burmese and Chin Hills (on the border between Burma and what is now Bangladesh) units in the area, though the total number of troops was much larger than that in the Japanese camp. Anand Pardhy and I wondered whether this high incidence was due to the fact that the Japanese soldiers were now eating predominantly British rations which would have a much lower fibre content than the Japanese had been consuming. Their own medical officers were equally surprised at the number of cases, and confirmed that appendicitis was normally a rarity. There is evidence that the incidence of appendicitis is greater in communities which consume a diet high in refined sugar and low in fibre compared to those which eat a diet high in fibre. Burkitt and Trowell[1] originally suggested an inverse relationship between appendicitis and the amount of fibre in the diet. This is confirmed by the fact that the incidence of appendicitis in British troops in India during the period 1936-1947 was approximately five times greater than in Indian troops.[2] In the same period the basic ration for Indian troops contained one third the amount of animal protein and three times as much high fibre foods (par-boiled rice, atta (unrefined wheat flour) and pulses (dal and peas)) as that of British soldiers in India.[3] Burkitt and Trowell also referred to reports that Sudanese troops in North Africa and West African troops in Singapore had an increased incidence of appendicitis when given British rations. However it is not clear from these reports whether this increased incidence was higher than or similar to that in communities with a low fibre diet. A rate of ten cases in six months for a population of 1000 men would give an annual incidence of 200 cases per 10,000 population. The incidence of appendicitis in England and Wales for the years 1931-1935 was 45 per 10,000, while the annual discharge rate for 1959 was 27 per 10,000, suggesting an incidence of around 35 per 10,000 for the 1940's, or one sixth the rate in the Japanese soldiers. The converse effect was recorded by van Ouwerkerk.[4] In the Dutch civilian internment camps in Indonesia during the 1939-1945 war appendicitis was practically unknown. The diet consisted of "rice in insufficient

47

quantities, unprocessed vegetables and practically without meat and fat".

During my stay in Prome I had a week's leave in Maymyo (1070 metres above sea level), a hill station named after Colonel May, a British officer in the Bengal Infantry who was stationed there in 1887. Maymyo was a cool and beautiful place where one could buy strawberries in the market. I was offered a trip in the back of a 15 cwt truck to Lashio on the road to China. We started off at night, coasting down the hills with the engine switched off; at first I thought this was to economise on petrol, but when I heard the clank of petrol cans at one of the stops I realised that the petrol saved was being sold. As we neared Lashio we met long lines of Chinese coolies carrying loads slung on a pole between two men. All were dressed in blue cotton trousers and jacket and all had large goitres. I found out later that the Shan Hills in East Burma was a recognised area of iodine-deficiency goitre.

One of my duties on return from leave was to submit an annual report to the A.D.M.S. in Rangoon. Feeling disgruntled because my repatriation had been delayed owing to a shortage of physicians, I added a rider that our unit was short of essential equipment and "neglected by those in authority". When Colonel Singh read it, he called me into his office, saying "You can't send this". I said that I thought it was true but if he, as a regular officer, would suffer I wouldn't send it, though as I hoped to be out of the Army quite soon it would not affect my military prospects. To his credit, the C.O. allowed my report to go forward and within a fortnight we had a visit by the A.D.M.S from Rangoon. About a month later and a week before I received my repatriation orders I was promoted to medical specialist, with the rank of major; what connexion, if any, there was between my report and my promotion I never knew. Among visitors to the C.C.S. was a three man graves registration unit; it was their grisly task to identify the bodies of allied troops in the jungle and to record the exact map references for later burial in a war cemetery.

At last it was time to go home. My new orderly, a newly recruited, naive youth from Bengal, asked me what kind of sandwiches I would like to take for the trip to Rangoon. "Egg and jam", I told him; "Yeggs and jam, Sahib", he repeated dutifully, and that is exactly what each sandwich contained. On the way to Rangoon my truck ran into a cow which was strolling across the road. The cow limped off the road bellowing loudly, but the foot brake refused to work after the collision. Annoyed with the driver for going too fast, I drove for the rest of the journey, using the gears and the handbrake. It seemed somehow a fittingly bathetic end to three years in India and South East Asia.

The voyage back on the S.S. Orontes was more comfortable than the outward trip. We arrived at Southampton in February 1947 in the middle of a particularly hard winter. The train to Waterloo had no heating and the frozen fields looked like Siberia. London was dirtier, more down-at-heel than I remembered it in the early 1940s. None of the telephone boxes were working and all the public clocks had stopped. My gold watch, which my father had given me, was stolen from my "digs". On my disembarkation leave, wearing my uniform to keep me warm, and with my mepacrine-yellow face, I felt I was being overcharged in the shops.

After my leave I spent a short time at the Cambridge Hospital in Aldershot, and in August 1947 I was demobilised. I couldn't bring myself to accept the "demob" pork pie hat which was on offer, and wandered round looking for a suit which didn't look like those which the inmates of mental hospitals used to wear. The sergeant in charge of "demob" clothing called me back. "You're in the wrong section, Sir, you're in "short portly".

Back in London I noticed in Sloane Square a small group in crumpled ill-fitting clothing; they were staring at the traffic in a bewildered manner. They were clearly "D.Ps" (displaced persons) and their eyes had the same "died inwardly" expression I had seen in the Royal Scots captain in Bombay three years previously.

REFERENCES
1. Burkitt D P , Trowell H C. Refined carbohydrate foods and disease. London: Academic Press, 1975. 92-4.
2. Medical Directorate, India. Reports on the health of the Army in India 1936-1947. New Delhi.
3. Medical Directorate, India. Field Service Hygiene Notes India. New Delhi, 1945. 111-14.
4. Van Ouwerkerk L W. Diet and appendicitis. Arch Chir Neerl 1951; 3: 164-78.

Appendix

The Origins and History of the Indian Medical Service and the Indian Army Medical Corps

The beginnings of the I.M.S.

THE FIRST MEDICAL officers in the East India Company were surgeons on board their ships. When factories had been established on the Coromandel Coast (South East India) and in Bengal in the seventeenth century a medical officer was appointed to each factory. In 1745, during the Anglo-French wars, medical officers accompanied the troops in the field.

In 1764 the Bengal Medical Service was established, with head surgeons, surgeons, and surgeon's mates. Madras followed suit in 1767, and Bombay in 1779. In 1824 the officers of the Bengal Medical Service were given the ranks of lieutenant colonel as a member of the Board, major as Superintendent Surgeon, and lieutenant as Assistant Surgeon. In 1857 Director Generals were appointed in Bombay, Madras and Bengal. In 1896 the medical services of the three Presidencies were combined in the Indian Medical Service (I.M.S.). In 1913 the head of the I.M.S. was designated Director of Medical Services.*

The organisation of the medical services in India

From the beginning the I.M.S. was primarily a military organisation whose function was the medical care of the Indian Army.

---

* What began with the three Presidencies of Madras, Bombay and Bengal was gradually extended during the nineteenth century by force of arms or peaceful annexation, leaving Hyderabad, Mysore, Kashmir, Gwalior and Baroda as independent states under Indian rulers. Civil surgeons of the I.M.S. were appointed to some of these states.

In 1796 the service was divided into military and civil branches, but all officers retained their military rank; those in 'civil employ' formed a reservoir for the Army. By 1865 the civil side was responsible for the medical care of the civil population (in practice this meant the higher ranking civil service officers and their families), public health, medical education and research, and administration of the jails. With the exception of a few academic posts, officers on the civil side could undertake private practice. In addition to posts with a medical function there was a postmaster, a cotton agent, a conservator of forests, and a naturalist. The non-medical posts were later abolished.

From the eighteenth century onwards problems arose about the duties, procedure, and scales of pay of the I.M.S. compared to the R.A.M.C. in India. In addition there was the Indian Medical Department (I.M.D.), formed in 1916 which consisted of a nucleus of British officers and Indian officers with Indian licentiate degrees* who acted as Sub-Assistant Surgeons with the ranks of captain and lieutenant, and the Indian Hospital Corps (I.H.C.) comprising Indian nurses and poorly trained nursing sepoys.

Between 1865 and 1943, there were fourteen Commissions, Schemes, Proposals, Committees, Reports, Recommendations and Missions to end the confusion in the medical services in India.

The 1914-1918 War caused further difficulties; R.A.M.C. officers were withdrawn from India to the United Kingdom, instead of the United Kingdom acting as a reserve for India. In addition, the War Office insisted that candidates for the R.A.M.C. in India should be of pure European blood and that Indians were not suited to medical care of British troops. Calls for the unification of the I.M.S. and the R.A.M.C. in India were rejected. In 1926 the Government of India sent a long despatch to the Secretary of State for India proposing that in the I.M.S. the ratio of British officers to Indian officers should be 3:1.

The formation of the Indian Army Medical Corps

In 1939 the military side of the I.M.S. was confined to medical supervision of garrisons, with a small number of medical officers

---

* Licentiates were doctors with qualifications from the minor medical colleges; graduates had studied at the Medical Schools of Bombay, Madras and Calcutta.

for active service units, primarily to operate on the North West Frontier. At this time there was a severe shortage of both graduate and licentiate Indian doctors. At the beginning of the war the I.M.S. consisted of 366 officers on the military side (223 British and 143 Indians) and 265 on the civil side. In addition there were 300 officers in the Army in India Reserve of Officers (A.I.R.O. [M]) and 291 in the Indian Reserve of Retired Officers (I.R.R.O.).

From June 1940 the demand for medical officers for the I.M.S. increased rapidly and recruitment for Emergency Commissions (I.M.S. [E.C.]) was started. In addition to these categories the following were recruited, European doctors in India and the United Kingdom, Assistant Surgeons in the I.M.D. (British cadre) and medical graduates in state or privately managed railways. In January 1942 women medical practitioners, a certain number of specialists, and civilian medical practitioners were recruited. In the following month non-medical anti-malaria officers were appointed.

In 1942 the I.M.D. was expanded by the recall of reservist Sub-Assistant Surgeons in civilian employment and the re-employment of those who had retired. Owing to the severe shortage of doctors non-medical officers were appointed as registrars and quartermasters in hospitals. In September 1942 the Indian Army was short of 793 doctors, and the Adjutant General suggested the regular dispatch of 50 doctors per month from the United Kingdom. The rapid increase in the strength of the I.M.S. is shown in fig. 3. In January 1943 a Committee under the Chairmanship of Brigadier A.F.G. Forbes was set up and completed its deliberations two months later. The Committee was of the opinion that the I.M.S., I.M.D. and I.H.C. should be amalgamated to form the I.A.M.C.; as a footnote the Committee expressed surprise that amalgamation had not taken place years earlier. Under the new arrangements I.M.S. officers were seconded to the I.A.M.C.; members of the I.M.D. and licentiates were given the improved status as officers in the I.A.M.C. which they had long been demanding. The training of nursing sepoys was to be improved and central depots were to be set up for the training of Indian medical officers and nursing sepoys.

At the beginning of the 1939 the possibility of war with Japan was not seriously considered until the attack on Pearl Harbor in December 1941, though the Indian Army was expected, as in the 1914-1918 war, to serve in Europe and other theatres outside India.

This account of the formation of the I.M.S. and the I.A.M.C. has been taken from the "Official History of the Indian Armed Forces in the Second World War, 1939 1945".[1] Additional information, of a more intimate nature is contained in the second and third editions of the Handbook on the I.M.S. published in 1912[2] and 1939[3] (the first edition was published in 1890); as it happens the books were written just before the outbreak of the First and Second World Wars and indicate the lack of preparedness for war in both instances.

In 1912 the medical officers in 'military employ' consisted of three medical officers for the Sappers and Miners, 38 for cavalry regiments, and 136 for infantry regiments. Under the direct control of the Army Department were a Surgeon Naturalist and the medical officer to the Lawrence Military Asylum at Sanawar in the Punjab; the latter had to be married and a member of the Church of England. The Surgeon Naturalist was attached to the Marine Survey and was engaged in biological research; during the marine surveying season he cruised in the Royal Indian Marine ship 'Investigator' and in the off season he worked in the museum in Calcutta.

A Civil Surgeon in 1912 was the Sanitary Officer (Public Health) for his district, Supervisor of dispensaries and their staff, Superintendent of the district jail, and the medico-legal expert for his district, "performing up to 200 post-mortems a year"; he was also in charge of the local lunatic asylum, and where appropriate Superintendent of a medical college for Sub-Assistant Surgeons (I.M.D.). For a fee he could be the medical officer for railways and mills, and could undertake private practice. In addition to these posts there were 20 plague officers mainly in the Punjab and Burma; they were concerned with "plague repression and prophylaxis". Plague officers (they were medically qualified) "have to spend the greater portion of their time touring in their districts, and the duties are arduous".

A newly commissioned lieutenant had to spend two years on the military side before he could apply for civil employment. He had to pass two courses at the R.A.M.C. College at Millbank, and Aldershot. On arrival in India he had to attend a course in practical sanitation under Indian conditions, and to pass an examination in Urdu. He also had to possess a "modern bacteriological microscope".

Special study leave was allowed for two years on full pay to go to Japan or Russia to study the language. The regulations governing leave, pay and behaviour were given in some detail: for example, a sword must not be worn in the hospital.

A fascinating section of the 1912 book consists of 48 pages at the end listing over 300 publications by Thacker, Spink and Company of Calcutta and Simla. Apart from military and medical subjects there are books on agriculture, religion, cooking and canary keeping. "Behind the Bungalow" by E H Aitken pokes gentle fun at Indian servants; a reviewer for "Home News" wrote "Of this book it may conscientiously be said that it does not contain a dull page, while it contains many which sparkle with bright and fascinating humour, refined with unmistakable evidence of culture". Another reviewer, in "Englishman" on "Sweets and how to make them; a handbook for Ladies everywhere, and more particularly in India", by Miss Pearson and Mrs Byrde, wrote "Every resident in India must prefer afternoon tea or a dessert fresh, sweet and daintily made. This little book will enable any mem-saheeb to minister to that reasonable preference".

The 1939 handbook is very different . Regulations governing pay, promotion and leave are given in greater detail. There is no longer any mention of "Chargers". Uniforms, service, mess dress and full dress are prescribed with actual measurements: collars for service dress should be "Van Heusen style (Indian shade) and for mess dress white linen wing collars. Spurs were to be worn by all field officers, officers holding a staff appointment and those on duty with a Field Ambulance. Spurs "must not be worn on board ship and will be removed when dancing". Full dress was no longer a required order of dress except for officers holding the appointments of Honorary Physician and Honorary Surgeon to the King, and Honorary Surgeon to the Viceroy. Plumes were to be worn as follows: for general officers black swan feathers drooping outwards, 10 inches long; for colonels the feathers should be 8 inches long, and for other officers 6 inches.

For natives of India who were candidates for a permanent appointment to the I.M.S. the candidate had to produce a horoscope and a 'family book' (presumably a family tree). The application form for British candidates for short service commissions in the I.M.S. included the following questions: "Do you consider that

54

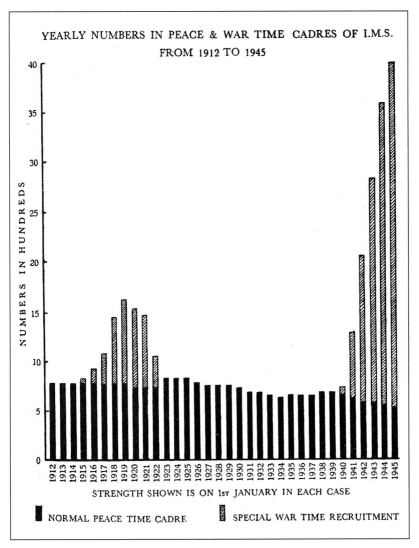

Figure 3
Figure reproduced from the "Official history of the Indian Armed
Forces in the Second World War 1939-45".

55

he shows tact in dealing with natives of India?", and, "Is he a good, bad or indifferent horseman?".

The variety of appointments available on the civil side was less than in 1912 but I.M.S. officers remained in charge of district jails; unusual appointments were the Superintendent of a 'Borstal' in Punjab and the Superintendent of a mental hospital in Lucknow.

In conclusion, taking into account the preoccupations of the I.M.S. in India in 1939 and the fact that in that year the armed forces in India numbered only 160,000 men in the Indian infantry and 60,000 British troops, the eventual achievement of an army of two and a half million and the parallel expansion of the army medical services in India were truly remarkable feats. (fig 3).

After partition in 1947 the I.M.S. ceased to exist in India and Pakistan, and the I.A.M.C. became the Army Medical Service (A.M.S.) in both countries.

REFERENCES
1. Raina B L (editor). Official history of the Indian Armed Forces in the Second World War, 1939-45; Medical Services vol. I Administration. Kanpur. Job Press, 1953.
2. Seton B G, Major, Gould J, Major. The Indian Medical Service. Calcutta and Simla. Thacker, Spink & Co., 1912.
3. Chopra A N, Major. Indian Medical Service: a Handbook. Government of India Press, New Delhi, 1939.

Index

Abdul Wali Khan, 37
Aden, 6
Appendicitis, 47-48
Army Medical Training Centre (India), (A.M.T.C.(I)), 18-21, 24-25
Ascariasis, 38, 40
Assam, 10-15
Atom bomb, 26
Auchinleck, 8-9

Bangalore, 7-9
Basu, 19
Bengal Medical Service, 50
Bennett, 12-13
Beri-Beri, 30-32
Bombay, 6-7
Bomford, 22
Burkitt, 47

Calcutta, 10, 16-17
Cameron Highlands, 42
Changi, 28-29, 32
Chindits, 13-15
Churchill, 20, 28
Crookham, 2

Dacca, 25
Dhaka, 25
Diphtheria, 15, 25, 30
Displaced Person (D.P.), 49
Dunlop, 1
Dysentery, 8, 14

Edinburgh, 2-3

Emlyn Williams, 5

Fergusson, 15
Fibre diet, 47-48

Gauhati, 10, 16
Goitre, 48
Golaghat, 11-15
Guwahati, 10, 16

Haora, 10, 17
Happy Feet, 31
Hawe, 12
Hely, 16-17
Hookworm, 38-39
Howrah, 10, 17

Indian Army Medical Corps (I.A.M.C.), 18, 24, 51-56
Indian Hospital Corps (I.H.C.), 51-52
Indian Medical Department (I.M.D.), 51-52
Indian Medical Service (I.M.S.), 19, 25, 50-56

Jorhat, 10-11

K-Ration, 14-15, 29
Karoa, 27, 29
Kolkata, 10, 16-17

Lake, 18, 22
Lehman, 5, 7
Lelean, 3

57

Madras Sappers and Miners, 22-23
Malacca, 35-39
Malaka, 35-39
Malaria, 3, 12, 22, 38, 44, 52
Maymyo, 48
Meiktila, 22
Membership of the Royal College of Physicians (M.R.C.P.), 1-2
Merriman, 20-22
Methyl alcohol, 34-36
Morris, 9, 12-13, 25
Mumbai, 6-7
Mysore, 21

Nilgiris, 21

Ootacamund, 21
Ooty, 21
Orontes, 49

Pardhy, 43, 47
Plague, 21, 53
Platt, 24
Pollock, 3-4
Poona, 7, 18-25
Port Said, 5-6
Prisoners of War (British), 27-34
Prisoners of War (Japanese), 44-48
Prome, 43-49
Pune, 7, 18-25
Pyinmana, 23

Ramchandra, 19

Rangoon, 24, 43
Released Allied Prisoners of War and Internees (R.A.P.W.I.), 29-34
Rosenheim, 39-40
Roundworm, 38, 40

Samson-Way, 18-19
Scrub Typhus, 13, 15, 44
Serajgonj, 10, 16
Singapore, 27-36
Smith (Smithy), 24-25
Spicer, 32, 34, 39
Stratheden, 4-5
Suez, 6

Throps, 40-42
Toungoo, 22-23
Tropical Medicine, 2-3
Trowell, 47

University College Hospital (U.C.H.), 1

VJ Day, 26

Walters, 21
Westcliffe on Sea, 3-4
Wingate, 13-15

Yangon, 24, 43
Yaws, 38

Zipper, 27, 29